Mathematical Applications
in Political Science
III

Mathematical Applications in Political Science

III

Edited by Joseph L. Bernd

With the assistance of Archer Jones

The University Press of Virginia

Charlottesville

Dedication

To my mother, Eva B. Bernd, and to the memory of my father, Laurence J. Bernd

Preface

THREE of the five papers[1] in this volume were first presented at the third conference on Mathematical Applications in Political Science, held at Virginia Polytechnic Institute, Blacksburg, Virginia, June 19–July 9, 1966. Two earlier conferences focusing on the same theme were held at Southern Methodist University, Dallas, Texas, in the summers of 1964 and 1965.[2] Four of the contributors, and the editor, are political scientists —Gerald H. Kramer and William H. Riker of the University of Rochester, Richard L. Merritt of the University of Illinois, and S. Sidney Ulmer of the University of Kentucky. Otto A. Davis is an economist and Melvin Hinich is a statistician; both are affiliated with Carnegie-Mellon University.

The conferences, supported by the National Science Foundation, were conceived to assist political scientists in learning how mathematical applications may be effectively utilized in their discipline. The meetings were designed to afford opportunities for the presentation of techniques and models involving statistical and mathematical applications and for high-level discussions devoted to determination of the limits and validity of these relatively advanced concepts as employed in political science. One hundred and eleven political scientists participated in the three conferences, and, to further the interdisciplinary design, ten conferees were

[1] The Kramer and the Merritt papers are not on the same subjects as those which these authors presented at the conference.

[2] For the four published papers of the 1964 conference, see John M. Claunch (ed.), *Mathematical Applications in Political Science* (Dallas: Arnold Foundation Monographs, Southern Methodist University, 1965). The contributors were Harold D. Guetzkow, William H. Riker, Donald E. Stokes, and S. Sidney Ulmer.

For the seven published papers of the 1965 conference, see Joseph L. Bernd (ed.), *Mathematical Applications in Political Science*, II (Dallas: Southern Methodist University Press, 1966). A paperback edition was published as an Arnold Foundation Monograph, Southern Methodist University, 1966. The contributors were Hayward R. Alker, Jr., Otto A. Davis and Melvin Hinich, Carl F. Kossack, Gerald H. Kramer, Richard L. Merritt, William H. Riker, and Frank S. Scalora.

included from economics, psychology, history, computer science, statistics, and mathematics.

This work has been made possible by the co-operation of a number of persons. Archer Jones, former Head of the Department of History and Political Science at Virginia Polytechnic Institute, was active in the planning of the volume and of the conference out of which it grew. Nack Y. An served as Associate Director of the conference. James A. Dator offered valuable suggestions after reading parts of the manuscript. Leslie F. Malpass, Dean of the College of Arts and Sciences, and Warren W. Brandt, Academic Vice President of Virginia Polytechnic Institute, displayed understanding of the problems of an editor. Lee Rutland, Head, Department of Mathematics, Virginia Polytechnic Institute, offered valuable technical advice regarding the publication of mathematical material. Typing assistance was furnished by Judi Snider of the secretarial staff of the Department of Mathematics. The advice and assistance of the members of the staff of the University Press of Virginia are appreciated.

The editor is solely responsible for any deficiencies in the conception and execution of the work.

March 22, 1967   JOSEPH L. BERND

Contents

Figures

Tables

Mathematical Applications in Political Science

III

contains enough critical sophistication to identify readily the limitations of the newer, behavioral departures. In consequence, it has not proved feasible to develop a new consensus to replace that which is being discarded, and confusion has so far triumphed over both error and truth. Empirical research is heavily emphasized, and competing, narrow-gauge theories have emerged in several subfields. Scholars often find that they are able to communicate only with colleagues in their own particular subfield, and not always with them. Competing groups in a particular subfield, as well as members of the profession in general, talk past each other without effective communication. Particularistic theories coexist in disconnected fragments. Political study is balkanized.[6]

A cursory examination of curriculums reveals that, despite what would appear to be a healthy awareness of methodological inadequacies,[7] formal preparation remains grossly inadequate. Recent Ph.D.'s from even the most renowned universities complain that they do not understand the sophisticated mathematics and statistics regularly found in journal articles. The problem of methods, however, is not limited to a hiatus between traditional political study and behavioralism. Eugene J. Meehan has observed that "the role of methodology in the teaching of political science is slight. Students enter and leave graduate school without even the most primitive kind of training in this area, without any conscious realization of its importance."[8]

The Role of Systematic Theory

At this point a word of clarification is in order. Although scientific progress in political study depends upon systematic theory, it should not be assumed, at least for the near term, that the resulting theory will offer a

[6] Albert Somit and Joseph Tanenhaus in *American Political Science: A Profile of a Discipline* (New York: Atherton Press, 1964), pp. 14–17, reveal survey findings that American students of politics are aware of inadequacies in the present state of their calling. A majority of respondents taking a position agree that "much that passes for scholarship is superficial or trivial," that "political scientists in the United States are unhappy about the current state of their discipline," that there is "no generally agreed upon body of methods and techniques," that "communication among political scientists tends to be seriously hindered by the inadequacy of their basic concepts," that "a high proportion of political scientists actually think of themselves as scientists only in a broad and figurative sense," that they do not engage in studies in which it is possible for one scholar to replicate findings of another, and the like.

[7] *Ibid.*

[8] *The Theory and Method of Political Analysis* (Homewood, Ill.: Dorsey Press, 1965), p. 2.

detailed and satisfying explanation of all things political. The present agglomeration of narrow-gauge and fragmented theories and concepts may be impressive if one ignores the inconsistencies, gaps, and confusions. The critical question is not whether a new system explains everything better, or even whether it explains everything. What is vital is whether it logically explains a preponderance of the most significant variables in a more satisfying way than does any other scheme and whether the theory provides effective machinery for developing a higher order of verified propositions, or for making predictions about political behaviors.

Economics: A Brief View of the State of the Discipline

Apparently, economists have been more successful than have political scientists in building bridges to connect local empirical findings to subfield theories and to connect these narrow theories to broad, systematic theory. Thus the "range and power" of economic analysis, to use Truman's apt phrase, are relevant throughout the economic system. Economists seem able to communicate effectively with one another. Terms like "discipline" and "science," as applied to economics, become more than charitable slogans. In the curriculum attention to methodology is emphatic and sophisticated, although (it may be pointed out) the extent and scope of mathematical training depend upon whether or not the student is aiming at econometrics.

In the Direction of Theoretical Synthesis: The Problem of Measurement

Some students of politics, as well as some economists who have studied political problems, believe that a science of politics may readily develop following lines laid down in economics. Others disagree. The critics emphasize, and the advocates generally concede, that the monetary unit offers to economics a unique measurement advantage, except in comparison with fields of politics in which votes or other decisions may be effectively quantified. Moreover, governments collect and publish indicators of economic decisions more systematically than they do political indicators. These handicaps should not be regarded as fatal to political measurements; other, less direct political indicators are discernible. Political decisions themselves are empirically evident, and variables related to these decisions are discoverable. In respect to considerations other than measurement, and not always here, politics is not inherently at a disadvantage in comparison with economics. Yet measurement is a scientific problem of major importance.

Measurement Problems in Relation to the Linkage of Abstract Theories and Empirical Appearances

Closely related to questions of measurement is the necessity that hypotheses derived from broad, systematic theory be tested empirically. Critics of systematic theory building and devotees of narrow-gauge subfield theory as a guide or adjunct to empirical research tend to suggest that broad-scope theory will of necessity be highly abstract and simplified, divorced from empirical verification, and unsatisfying in explaining the variables that appear in the real world. Yet this problem appears to have been overcome in economics and in the physical sciences. The obstacle may not be insuperable for a science of politics, if hypotheses, logically derived from systematic theory, may be empirically tested in ways which permit measurements of satisfying precision.

Hobbes described the knowledge of abstract models in relation to empirical appearances as "conditional knowledge." Admittedly, this conditional knowledge is not reality, but, in the words which William T. Bluhm uses to explain Hobbes, if "we are good at fitting . . . the right general names to the fancies which inhabit our psyches and if the rules we establish correspond to empirical laws," we shall have powerful instruments for prediction and control.[9]

The Limits of Historical Variation

David Easton suggests that the abstractness of the Hobbesian model is a major weakness, depriving it of utility for empirical social science.[10] Yet this criticism of logical-deductive models may be applied also to empirical-inductive models. Consequently, it is not clear that Easton's criticism of the former alone has merit. Narrow-gauge theories may appear to "fit the facts" more closely than a general systems theory, but it is well to remember that theory on any level is a simplification that does not explain all variable aspects of reality. At least since the time of Hume it has been demonstrable in philosophy that there is not a one-to-one relationship between any theory and any fact, or between fact and fact. However persuasive the theory, however spectacular the use of it, it is an example of the fallacy of misplaced concreteness to equate it with reality.[11]

[9] *Theories of the Political System* (Englewood Cliffs, N.J.: Prentice-Hall, 1965), pp. 267–70.

[10] *Op. cit.*, pp. 8–10.

[11] Alfred North Whitehead is responsible for the concept of "misplaced concreteness," which he uses in a different but related sense. See *Science and the Modern World*

Research which purports to derive its findings strictly from historical data labors under special difficulties, which have been identified by the authors of *The American Voter:*

If theory can guide historical descriptions, *the historical context of most research on human behavior places clear limitations on the development of theory.* In evolving and testing his theoretical hypotheses the social scientist usually must depend on what he is permitted to observe by the progress of history. The experimental scientist often escapes this problem, at least in verifying his theoretical statements, by manipulating the variables of his theory. *But the variables of large-scale social processes can rarely be manipulated in research, and the historical reality with which the social scientist must deal typically yields data that are inadequate for developing and testing a fully elaborated theory.* Their inadequacy has to do partly with the problem of controlling factors: *when he examines the relation of two or more variables a social scientist is seldom able to remove by experimental or statistical devices the effects of all additional factors that may influence the variable of immediate interest. But the inadequacy of "natural" data has to do also with what might be called the problem of limited variation.* If we return to the idea that theory consists of statements of the inter-relationships of variables, it is evident *variables of great importance in human affairs may exhibit little or no change in a given historical period. As a result, the investigator whose work falls in this period may not see the significance of these variables and may fail to incorporate them in his theoretical statements. And even if he does perceive their importance, the absence of variation will prevent a proper test of hypotheses that state the relation of these factors to other variables of his theory.*[12]

The theorist may transcend the limitations of historical variation by logical analysis of variables which have not appeared in the historical evidence and by speculation.[13] Indeed, such logical and speculative analysis appears essential for a policy science if it is to exceed the confines of strict empiricism. Yet speculation exacts a price; speculative theories are not subject to verification. The requirement that a policy science speculate, coupled with the scientific requirement that theories be testable, suggests a possible division of labor and conceptualization between the policy science and the pure science functions of political science.

If speculating policy scientists become policy-makers, they will be able (as do economic policy-makers who have the ear of governments) to put their theories into operation. Thus speculative theorizing may lead

(New York: New American Library of World Literature, 1948, originally published by Macmillan, 1925), pp. 52–59.

[12] Angus Campbell, Phillip E. Converse, Warren E. Miller, and Donald E. Stokes, *The American Voter* (New York: John Wiley & Sons, 1960), pp. 9–10; emphasis added.

[13] Simulation is, of course, an alternative experimental means of testing hypotheses in structured social situations. The device is limited because the costs of information and subjects impose rather narrow boundaries on the testing situations. Another limitation is artificiality—it is *simulation*, not historical reality.

both to opportunities and dangers in the real world: new theories can be tested.

Awareness of these limitations on both broad and narrow theory imposes special obligations on political science. As the study of politics moves, hopefully, toward the development of scientific and systematic theory, it behoves each student of politics meaningfully to relate the theoretical and the empirical, to emphasize the need for attention to methodology in the curriculum, and emphatically to enter upon the quest for bridges which may connect the unconnected and communicate the uncommunicated. In this spirit, it is hoped that some common threads may be found in the five papers which comprise this volume.

Focus of the Papers

Four of the five papers (excluding Kramer's) center on the problem of enhancing precision in various aspects of measurement. Two papers—those by Davis and Hinich and by Riker—employ the concept of rationality used in economics. Kramer's paper focuses directly on the rationality concept and explores a major difficulty of its use. The use of models for predicting decisional behavior is explicitly or implicitly recognized as an aim in all five papers. The authors in common recognize that mathematics and statistics significantly contribute to the precision of their concepts.

Otto A. Davis and Melvin Hinich

Davis and Hinich extend the analysis of a logical-deductive model of the election system which they had developed earlier.[14] The model conceives of decisions by parties, candidates, and voters as rational in the economic sense, i.e., as designed to maximize utility income in terms of winning elections (for parties and candidates) and in serving perceived self-interest (in the case of voters). While the paper does not subject the hypotheses of the model to empirical testing, it does come to grips directly with the kind of problem which an empirical test would necessarily encounter. The original model employed the simplifying assumption that all voters assign the same degree of importance to each issue. Voters might, for instance, support or oppose integrated schools, but "the model does not allow some voters to be concerned while others do

---

[14] "A Mathematical Model of Policy Formation in a Democratic Society," in Joseph L. Bernd (ed.), *Mathematical Applications in Political Science*, II (Dallas: Southern Methodist University Press, 1966), 175–208.

not care whether or not the schools are integrated." The refined model seeks to be more realistic regarding the "weight of importance" variable. Recognizing the excessive difficulty of assigning possibly differing positive definite matrices to individual voters, David and Hinich suggest the notion of an "average" importance for any given issue for any universe of voters.[15]

The device proposes a solution which readily measures intensity of interest as well as the identity and nature of voter preference. The averaging device may constitute a major tool in the difficult task of building bridges to link abstract models with empirically derived quantities. This nexus is obviously critical for relating systematic theory to empirical research in terms which may be scientifically meaningful.

Gerald H. Kramer

An important concept, employed in economics and sometimes applied to political decision-making, is the notion of rational choice. In the economic sense, the rationality of ends may not be judged, only means to a given end are rational. Rationality refers to the choice of the most efficient means for attaining an end. In economics and in political applications of the concept, maximization of utility income is usually posited as the desired end. Means, therefore, are rational if they maximize efficiency in attaining utility income. The rationality model typically assumes that choices may be transitively ordered, that complete information about variables is available on which to base choices, and that computations leading to rational decisional choices are performable.

Rationality models have been devised to deal with some of the basic problems raised by the assumptions. For instance, insufficiency of information and corresponding uncertainty may make a rational decision impossible, or the prohibitive cost of information may mean that the decision-maker does not or cannot pay the price for information which would, presumably, make possible a rational decision.

Herbert Simon has raised a question as to the utility of the assumption that the decision-maker is able to handle the complex computations required for a rational decision: "Broadly stated, the task is to replace the global rationality of economic man with a kind of rational behavior that is compatible with the access to information and the computational capacities that are actually possessed by organisms, including man, in the kinds of environments in which such organisms exist." [16]

[15] Page 17, below.
[16] "A Behavioral Model of Rational Choice," in *Models of Man* (New York: John Wiley & Sons, 1957), 241.

The paper by Gerald H. Kramer carries the question a step further:

The validity of the theory of decision-making does not directly depend on whether decision-makers really have consistent preference orderings, or actually perform complicated calculations; the theory asserts only that they behave *as if* they did. Even if real decision-makers in every-day environments cannot perform the calculations required for a comprehensive analysis of their problems and instead rely on simple rules of thumb or other devices to guide their choices, it may nevertheless be true that these simpler rules lead them to behave as if they were acting rationally, at least to a reasonable approximation.[17]

Kramer applies a formal test to determine whether a finite information-processing device, or automation, is capable of behaving rationally. He asks "whether there is any *conceivable* program for such a device which could lead to input-output behavior consistent with the theory of decision-making." [18] For this purpose Kramer uses the theory of finite automata.

William H. Riker

In the paper presented here William H. Riker reports on experimental findings which test hypotheses derived from models of games featuring three-person bargaining. The logical-deductive model predicts how players, if they are rational in the economic sense, will divide the rewards offered in the game. Strictly speaking, the game is more "economic" than "political," but these terms indicate the ambivalence of the situation rather than its inherent quality. Bargaining and coalition formation are "political" processes by definition if they refer to the allocation of political values.

The findings reveal that the model for a three-person, zero-sum (or constant-sum) game has superior, but not perfect, predictive value. In a word, the tests indicate the probability, rather than the certainty, that the model is capable of predicting the bargaining solution that will be chosen, given any set of players under the conditions specified. The tests validate once more the propensity of some political actors to behave rationally some of the time. It is clear from this and other empirical evidence that in a certain sense politics is a science of probability, as, indeed, any science is probabilistic insofar as it is empirical and predictive. Rationality may explain an important element of political variance, but a significant residual variance remains to be explained via other concepts.

Riker notes that his models have "normative" significance, by which

---

[17] See p. 41, below.   [18] See p. 41, below.

he means that the models describe how players *ought* to behave if they hope to bargain successfully. It is also a positive model in that it purports to describe how in fact subjects in bargaining situations *do actually* behave. Indeed, the tests are designed to test whether in fact they behave according to the model, i.e., in a rational way. Riker tells us the model is descriptive as well as normative.[19]

The point is worth some attention because any theory, or model, inevitably carries value implications which exert influence on the nature of the product. Understanding the values, or biases, of a theory is necessary for assessing the impact of such values, or biases, on policy. Our best conception of science requires reduction, elimination, and control for the impact of values, but insofar as a residuum of value remains it should be explicitly identified and assessed.

S. Sidney Ulmer

The study by S. Sidney Ulmer differs from the previously described papers in this volume in terms of framework and method, but the Ulmer work is perhaps more representative of the empirical emphasis which currently characterizes behavioral research in politics. The author is concerned with the identification and analysis of variables by means of a model that is capable of predicting the decisions of judges. He uses historical data and he seeks to refine earlier predictive models in order to predict more accurately. His approach is essentially inductive by contrast with the logical-deductive models employed by Davis and Hinich, Kramer, and Riker.

Given the sharpness of the divergence, one is surprised to discern a number of elements shared by the Ulmer paper and the others, especially Riker's. For Ulmer, as for Riker, the findings are probabilities, not absolutes. The model does not predict perfectly. "Prediction is estimation," says Ulmer,[20] and, it may be added, estimation is a problem of measurement. The probabilistic dimension poses once again a problem of residual variance.

Unlike Riker, Ulmer does not employ the rationality standard. His purpose is to develop a predictive device from empirical material and then to test it. Riker, on the other hand, is discovering and measuring experimental deviation in order to test a logical standard, rational in that it is supposed to represent the most efficient behavior for bargaining subjects who want to share monetary rewards.

Yet at the end of his paper Ulmer does suggest the employment of

---

[19] See p. 66, below.   [20] See p. 87, below.

predictive judicial models for a purpose somewhat similar to that of Riker: "Finally, some emphasis should be placed on the reverse of the question usually posed by models for predicting court decisions. Whereas these models ask: What factors are predictors of decisions? one might ask: Given certain factors that ought to govern decision, what is the relative position of each judge or each court to the ideal of consistency?"[21]

Thus Ulmer phrases a question in reverse of the one he has been asking and in doing so comes close to paralleling Riker's original question. Ulmer's final comment suggests a norm by which the deviation of individual judges, and courts, may be measured and corrected in the interest of some public policy. Although the respective focuses of Ulmer and of Riker are normative, there is this difference: Ulmer's final comment is normative in the sense that he poses a standard for measuring the deviation or correlation with an a priori end, some given public policy. Riker's normative quest is directed toward an end which is logical, as distinguished from a priori. In other words, Riker's subjects will act in a certain logical or rational way in order to secure a monetary recompense, provided other players in the game are also rational. Ulmer's concept is normative in the sense that this is the way that judges ought to decide cases in the interest of a given policy. Riker's concept is normative in the sense that this is the way one ought to play the game if one wishes to win. The difference, however, may be more apparent than real. If sanctions are applied in Ulmer's case to punish deviant judges, then his subjects, like those of Riker, will be rational in order to be successful, i.e., to avoid sanctions. Thus, in a sense the two approaches, sharply differing in original conceptualization, ultimately agree not only in their normative interest but also in regard to the applicability of the rationality concept. The coincidence is significant in that a bridge for communication is opened in terms of political concepts between widely differing research approaches—the empirical-inductive and the logical-deductive.

Ulmer's paper coincides with the other papers in another significant respect. Like the logical-deductive model builders, he avoids the subjective quicksand of causal psychological analysis. In focusing on the problem of prediction, he identifies "indicators," rather than "psychological causes" of behavior. His indicators are variables which appear to be significant clues to the decisions, but they are not necessarily efficient causes of the decisions. Ulmer carefully points out that these indicators may be "effects," as well as "causes," the chicken or the egg.[22] There is, he says, no question of specifying cause and effect. The model "simply

[21] See p. 95, below.   [22] See p. 87, below.

asks whether the scores are indicators to the decisions." The approach that he employs is one which is increasingly resorted to by sophisticated social scientists (1) because causal findings are not susceptible to empirical verification (Hume) and (2) because causal verification is not essential to successful use of predictive models.

Richard L. Merritt

"Visual Representation of Mutual Friendliness" is devoted to content analysis of public opinion in several Western European countries regarding major foreign countries. Unlike Ulmer, whose focus is also empirical, Merritt utilizes psychological theory to explain causation. Thus the questions are designed to elicit immediate "visceral" responses rather than "intellectual" ones which are the product of unhurried reflection and analysis. Individual thought patterns are assumed to be both unimodal and bimodal. Responses are related causally to contemporary historical events. For instance, attitudes toward the Soviet Union are less friendly following the ruthless suppression of the Hungarian revolt but they become more favorable following Soviet achievements in space exploration. The rationality concept, significant in the papers of Davis and Hinich, Kramer, and Riker, is not relevant in Merritt's because the latter uses assumptions drawn from social psychology rather than economics and because he seeks explanations which fit a social psychological view of causation rather than a rationalist view.

A worthwhile comparative analysis with findings of relevance to general political (and social) science theory might result if these assumptions and aims were to be reversed, i.e., if Merritt's data were to be analyzed in the light of rationalist assumptions about causation and if social psychological theory were to be applied to the data of, for instance, Riker's paper.

Merritt's paper shares one point of conceptual emphasis which is of vital significance in all of the other papers in this volume except Kramer's. Precision in measurement is crucial. Measurements of data designed to indicate the causal relationships existing among facts are revealed in terms of probabilities, not absolutes. For instance, the answers of respondents to questions about their attitudes toward the Soviet Union are relative and approximate only. Obviously there may be a few instances in which a respondent has given much study to the question in advance of the coincidence of its being asked, so that his response is really "intellectual" and not "visceral."

Merritt's paper, like the others, is oriented by the common requirement of a policy science to assist statesmen who, in making decisions, must take cognizance of the probable consequences. The ability to predict is based on a perception of sequential patterns in human behavior and on an expectation of the persistence of such patterns.

Final Introductory Comment

Even a cursory treatment, such as the foregoing, reveals possibilities, as well as serious problems, for those who would attempt a theoretical synthesis in the interest of a science of politics. In this introductory essay an attempt has been made to identify some possible opportunities for synthesis. It should be emphasized, however, that the five papers in this volume are significant in their own right as original contributions to knowledge in their respective fields. Davis and Hinich have extended their earlier application of a model for the election system. Kramer has identified a serious problem of conceptualization for decision-making which assumes a rational capacity in the decision-maker. Riker reports experimental findings which support a rational model for bargaining. Ulmer has developed an apparently superior model for identifying variables of judicial decision-making and for predicting decisions. Merritt has analyzed perceptions of mutual friendliness respecting contemporary nation states in the light of social psychological theory about human responses and thought patterns.

Some Results Related to a Mathematical Model of Policy Formation in a Democratic Society *

1 Otto A. Davis and Melvin Hinich †
Carnegie-Mellon University

1. Introduction

IF ONE takes a grand view of the progress of science, both social and physical, there seems to be a high correlation between major advances in knowledge and the use of abstract and mathematical methods of thought. It appears doubtful that this correlation is spurious; and students in the social sciences, for example, political science, are sometimes exhorted and advised to turn their efforts to the development and empirical testing of analytically rigorous models.[1] Of course, the adoption of such a methodological approach to the study of real phenomena implies a commitment to the practice of making and accepting simplifying assumptions that reduce the complexity of the real problems under consideration. Aside from the issues of empirical testing, the mere construction of a model based upon some set of given assumptions raises some questions. First, there is the issue of whether the set of assumptions is "reasonable" for the problem at hand. Second, there is the question of whether certain of the assumptions of a model are crucial for its implications or results. In other words, it sometimes happens that the results can be derived from a weaker set of assumptions. These two questions, or issues, provide the motivation for this paper.

In a recent paper the authors developed a mathematical model of political choice which aimed at exploring the relationship between the policies adopted by a democratic government and the desires of the voters in the society.[2] This paper hopes to strengthen the implications of

* This research was supported by a grant from Resources for the Future to the Graduate School of Industrial Administration, Carnegie-Mellon University.
† Mr. Hinich is also a consultant to Hudson Laboratories, Columbia University.
[1] See, e.g., the comments by William H. Riker, *The Theory of Political Coalitions* (New Haven: Yale University Press, 1962), chap. i.
[2] See Otto A. Davis and Melvin Hinich, "A Mathematical Model of Policy Formation in a Democratic Society," in Joseph L. Bernd (ed.), *Mathematical Applications in Political Science*, II (Dallas: Southern Methodist University Press, 1966), 175–208.

some of the theorems established there. First, one of the restrictive assumptions used in the previous paper is relaxed. It is then shown that, under certain conditions, the major result still obtains, at least on the level of a suitable approximation. Finally, an argument is developed which attempts to establish the plausibility of the basic model.

2. A Review of the Basic Assumptions and Tools of Analysis

It is assumed that, at least conceptually, policies can be measured by certain indexes. While the number of variables (or indexes) which represent any given issue of policy is somewhat arbitrary and depends upon the sophistication of the individual viewing the issue in the sense that more or fewer dimensions might be relevant, it is presumed that the population of registered voters is homogeneous in that the same indexes measure any given policy for all voters. Further, it is assumed that each voter has preferences concerning all issues of policy and that the ith voter's preferred position (or set of most desired policies) can be represented by the column vector

$$x_i = [x_{i1}, x_{i2}, \ . \ . \ . \ , x_{in}]'$$

where the components x_{ik} represent the desired values of the indexes which measure given policies. Similarly, the column vector

$$\theta_j = [\theta_{j1}, \theta_{j2}, \ . \ . \ . \ , \theta_{jn}]'$$

represents the position or platform of the jth candidate or party.

Provision is made for the utility loss experienced by any voter when the government does not adopt his preferred set of policies. This is accomplished through the introduction of a loss function. Let θ represent an n-component column vector which represents governmental policy. Then the loss function of the ith voter is given by the quadratic form

$$(2.1) \qquad L_i(\theta) = (x_i - \theta)'A(x_i - \theta)$$

where, at least in the referenced paper, A was taken to represent a symmetric, positive definite matrix of rank n which is common to all voters.

Finally, the population of voters can be characterized by presuming that the preferred positions of all voters have been plotted into an n-dimensional frequency and that this frequency has been suitably normalized into a density $f_x(x)$. As a matter of notation, the relevant parameters are characterized as follows:

$$(2.2) \qquad E(x) = \mu_x$$

where E represents the expectation operator so that μ_x is the n-component column vector of means. Also,

(2.3) $E(x - \mu_x)(x - \mu_x)' = \Sigma$

where Σ is an nxn symmetric matrix whose components along the main diagonal are variances and the other elements are covariances.[3]

Certain norms are also used in the analysis. Let z represent an n-component column vector. Then the norm of the vector z with respect to the matrix A is defined and distinguished by the following notation:

(2.4) $\|z\|_A = \sqrt{z'Az}$

so that the norm of the same vector with respect to the matrix $A\Sigma A$ is given by

(2.5) $\|z\|_{A\Sigma A} = \sqrt{z'A\Sigma Az}$

and the Euclidian norm is given by

(2.6) $\|z\|_I = \sqrt{z'Iz}$

where I represents the identity matrix of appropriate dimension.[4]

3. On the Representation of Variable Levels of Concern

Observe that in the definition (2.1) of individual loss functions the matrix A is assumed to be common to all voters. This assumption, which was used in most of the developments in the basic model which was presented in our recent paper,[5] is rather strong and has some restrictive implications. In particular, it implies that the population of voters is homogeneous. In other words, although no restrictions are placed upon the preferred points x_i (although the x_i must be describable by a density $f_x(x)$) so that individual voters are allowed to desire widely differing policies, the assumption implies that all voters assign the same relative weight to any given issue. As an illustration, one might consider the issue of segregation in the schools. The model would allow some voters to desire segregated schools and other voters integrated ones. However, the assumption that the matrix A is common to all voters implies that all assign the same degree of importance to the issue so that the model does not allow some voters to be concerned while others do not care whether or not the schools are integrated.

Granted the particular assumption that the matrix A is common to all

---

[3] In (2.3) and throughout this paper the notation prime (') represents the operation of transposition.

[4] Note that some of the notation used here, especially that for the mean (2.2) and for the norms, differs from that used in Davis and Hinich, *op. cit.*

[5] Section 6 assumed two loss functions with respective matrices A_1 and A_2 which had the property $A_1A_2 = 0$ so that there was no interaction between them.

voters, it was shown in our recent paper that the vector μ_x of the means of preferred points exerts a powerful influence upon the policy choices of candidates in an election. Specifically, if the density $f_x(x)$ is multivariate normal, the vector μ_x is a dominant strategy, and also, if μ_x is not chosen by either party, the candidate choosing a policy vector "nearer" to μ_x than the other candidate wins the election. In addition, no matter what the density $f_x(x)$, the vector μ_x becomes more and more powerful as the number of components (or issues) of the vectors x_i (and μ_x and θ) grows toward infinity while the matrix A remains positive definite.

It is obviously important to attempt to determine whether these conclusions remain unaltered when the particular assumption of a common A is weakened. Quite clearly different individuals do not always assign the same degree of importance to any given issue. Yet the decision to allow individual loss functions to vary in this respect is not easily transferable into a tractable model. Perhaps the most obvious and natural method would be to assign possibly differing positive definite matrices A_i to individual voters. Such a step, however, leads to a model whose high level of complexity appears to prohibit the attainment of analytical results. Accordingly, a far more simple method is utilized here.

It can be argued, of course, that although tastes differ with respect to the importance or weight assigned by various individuals to given issues of policy, the notion of an average importance, for any given issue, is both important and viable. In other words, with no restrictions upon the preferred points x_i, it is possible to consider the average levels (in a relative sense) of concern for various issues of policy. In order to make the point clearer, consider an extension of the previous example. Some voters simply may not care whether the schools are integrated or not, but others will feel concerned over this issue, with some desiring segregated and some integrated schools. Yet it is possible to think of computing some relative average of some index measuring the level of concern of the voters on this issue.

This notion of the average concern or importance or weight is used in the conceptualization of varying tastes among individuals. Specifically, it is assumed that for all issues there exists some average level of concern and that these averages can be summarized and represented by a matrix. Individual variations are represented as deviations from these averages. In other words, consider the matrix equation

$$(3.1) \qquad A = \bar{A} + \epsilon$$

where $\bar{A}$ is an nxn, symmetric, positive definite matrix and where ϵ represents an nxn matrix of stochastic elements denoted by ϵ_{ij}. It is assumed that these stochastic components ϵ_{ij} are independently distributed with

mean zero and a common variance σ_ϵ^2. This last assumption, like many of
the others which will be introduced, is not necessary to the argument but
adds greatly to notational simplicity. Note especially that in the representation (3.1), with $\bar{A}$ being given, the matrix A is stochastic.

Careful consideration should be given to (3.1) before it is accepted as
an adequate conceptualization of the phenomenon of differing individual
concerns with various issues of public policy. There is, of course, the problem of interpretation, and (3.1) enjoys two alternative possibilities. First,
for any individual whose loss function is given by (2.1) where the matrix
A in that loss function is given by (3.1), one might say that the individual's level of concern for each of the n issues of policy is so subject to
change that it can be viewed, essentially, as being given by a draw from a
specified probability distribution. This interpretation suffers, however,
from a violation of the well-known fact that individuals' attitudes tend
to be stable, at least over short periods of time. Under this alternative
interpretation, consider selecting a voter at random from the entire population of voters. Since the level of concern for each of the issues of policy
can vary from individual to individual, the matrix ϵ, and hence A, can be
looked upon as if they were stochastic. Under the assumptions specified
above,

(3.2) $E(\epsilon) = 0$

so that

(3.3) $E(A) = \bar{A}.$

If one selects a voter at random from the population, then one "expects"
to obtain an individual whose level of concern for each of the issues of
policy is average for the population.[6]

Given this particular interpretation of the randomness of the matrix ϵ,
there remains the problem of specifying the relationship between ϵ and
the vectors x, the preferred points of the voters in the population. The
simplest assumption, which is the one adopted here, is that ϵ and x are
independent. Behaviorally, this assumption means that if one selects a
voter from the population and determines his preferred point, then this
knowledge of the preferred point gives one no information in regard to
how the voter's level of concern for each of the issues of policy differs
from the average for the population. The x and ϵ do not vary in a systematic manner in their relationship with each other.

It might be observed that this assumption of independence, which is

---

[6] The usual convention of allowing E to represent the expectation operator is followed here.

made merely for analytical convenience, has an implication which seems at first glance to be at odds with one of the seldom-questioned propositions of social-psychological folklore. This proposition has it that any given individual is more likely to feel intensely about an issue if he has an extreme, rather than a moderate, position on that issue. Accordingly, independence appears inappropriate. Two points are relevant here. First, one can question the proposition. It might be, for example, that because of problems associated with measurement and identification the relevant studies have not been able to identify existing individuals who have extreme positions but nonintense feelings on given issues. Second, and certainly more important, the proposition states that intensity of feeling is associated with extreme positions; and it obviously is necessary to consider both ends (or left and right) of the extreme. Thus, if the proposition from the folklore is accepted, one should have relatively large and positive values of the components of the stochastic matrix ϵ associated with those values of the components of x which are relatively distant from the mean μ_x in both directions. In other words, there may be a zero correlation although the two are not really independent. Nevertheless, if the basic symmetry of the relationship with regard to both extremes for given issues is admitted, then one can see from the developments which follow that the final result is not different from that which is obtained under the assumption of independence. Gains will be balanced by losses. Accordingly, the much simpler procedure of making the analytically convenient assumption of independence is followed here.

Finally, there is a somewhat subtle problem, which merits careful consideration, in regard to the specification (3.1) of the matrix A. In our recent paper, where it was assumed that the matrix A was common to all voters, A was presumed to be positive definite. This presumption ensured the nonnegativity of the loss function (2.1). Obviously, since zero utility losses represent the best that one can do because of the very nature of loss functions, the possibility of negative losses must be viewed with some alarm. It is assumed here that the matrix $\bar{A}$ is positive definite. However, since ϵ is assumed to be stochastic, it is easily seen from (3.1) that the positive definiteness of A is no longer assured; hence the problem of negative utility losses must be considered carefully.

Imagine selecting a voter at random from the population. Then, conditional on x,

$$(3.4) \qquad E[(x - \theta)' \, \epsilon (x - \theta)|x] = 0$$

and, since (3.4) obtains for all x,

$$(3.5) \qquad E[(x - \theta)'A(x - \theta)] = (x - \theta)'\bar{A}(x - \theta).$$

Since $\bar{A}$ is positive definite, one expects "on the average" to have loss functions which are everywhere nonnegative.

Unfortunately, this result (3.5) is not sufficient for the presumption that (3.1) is an adequate specification. One also needs to know something about the probability of obtaining a loss function which would allow negative losses. Consider

$$(3.6) \quad \text{Var}[(x - \theta)'A(x - \theta)|x] = E[((x - \theta)'\,\epsilon(x - \theta))^2|x]$$

or, in other terms, the conditional variance.[7] In order to simplify the notation, let the vector Δ be defined as follows:

$$(3.7) \qquad\qquad \Delta = x - \theta$$

where Δ_i will be used to represent the ith component of Δ. Then

$$(3.8) \qquad\qquad \Delta'\,\epsilon\Delta = \sum_i \sum_j \Delta_i\,\Delta_j\,\epsilon_{ij}$$

and, conditional on x (but omitting this bit of notation for convenience),

$$(3.9) \qquad E[(\Delta'\,\epsilon\Delta)^2] = E\left[\left(\sum_i \sum_j \Delta_i\,\Delta_j\,\epsilon_{ij}\right)^2\right].$$

It is easily seen that (3.9) can be written

$$(3.10) \qquad E[(\Delta'\,\epsilon\Delta)^2] = \sum_i \sum_j \Delta_i^2\,\Delta_j^2\,E(\epsilon_{ij}^2),$$

and it follows from the fact that

$$(3.11) \qquad\qquad E(\epsilon_{ij}^2) = \sigma_\epsilon^2$$

by definition, that the right-hand side of (3.10) becomes

$$(3.12) \qquad \sigma_\epsilon^2 \sum_i \sum_j \Delta_i^2\,\Delta_j^2 = \sigma_\epsilon^2 \left(\sum_i \Delta_i^2\right)^2.$$

In summary,

$$(3.13) \qquad E[((x - \theta)'\,\epsilon(x - \theta))^2|x] = \sigma_\epsilon^2\|x - \theta\|_I^4$$

where

$$(3.14) \qquad\qquad \|x - \theta\|_I = \sqrt{(x - \theta)'I(x - \theta)}$$

[7] In this notation, Var represents the operation of determining the variance of the expression in the brackets. Similarly, the notation SD is used later on to represent the standard deviation.

and I represents the identity matrix. Thus (3.13) represents nothing more than expressing (3.12) in the notation of the norm and giving a concise expression for the conditional variance (3.6). Obviously,

$$(3.15) \qquad SD\left[\|x - \theta\|_\epsilon^2\, |x\right] = \sigma_\epsilon \|x - \theta\|_I^2$$

where SD represents the standard deviation of the expression in the brackets.

It is desirable to relate the standard deviation σ_ϵ of the random variables ϵ_{ij} to the matrix $\bar{A}$. Let $\bar{\lambda}_{\min}$ represent the minimum eigenvalue of $\bar{A}$. Obviously, $\bar{\lambda}_{\min} > 0$ since $\bar{A}$ is positive definite. Let it be assumed that σ_ϵ is much less than $\bar{\lambda}_{\min}$, or in symbols

$$(3.16) \qquad \sigma_\epsilon \ll \bar{\lambda}_{\min}.$$

Given assumption (3.16), it follows that

$$(3.17) \qquad \sigma_\epsilon \|x - \theta\|_I^2 \ll \bar{\lambda}_{\min} \|x - \theta\|_I^2 < \|x - \theta\|_{\bar{A}}^2$$

where

$$(3.18) \qquad \|x - \theta\|_{\bar{A}}^2 = (x - \theta)'\bar{A}(x - \theta).$$

It follows from (3.15) and (3.17) that

$$(3.19) \qquad SD\left[\|x - \theta\|_\epsilon^2\, |x\right] \ll \|x - \theta\|_{\bar{A}}^2,$$

and since (3.19) obtains for all x

$$(3.20) \qquad SD\left[\|x - \theta\|_\epsilon^2\right] \ll \|x - \theta\|_{\bar{A}}^2.$$

Given the specification (3.1) of the matrix A, the loss function (2.1) can be written

$$(3.21) \quad (x - \theta)'A(x - \theta) = \|x - \theta\|_A^2 = \|x - \theta\|_{\bar{A}}^2 + \|x - \theta\|_\epsilon^2$$

in which the extreme right-hand side makes it easy to observe that the issue of whether the loss function can ever become negative depends upon whether the random term $\|x - \theta\|_\epsilon^2$ can become sufficiently negative to overpower the always nonnegative term $\|x - \theta\|_{\bar{A}}^2$. It is clear, however, from (3.20) that such an event has low probability, given the assumption (3.16), so that

$$(3.22) \qquad P\left\{\|x - \theta\|_A^2 < 0\right\}$$

is small. Further, this probability can be made arbitrarily small by restricting σ_ϵ to be small in relation to $\bar{\lambda}_{\min}$. Given the ordinal nature of utility measurements, it can be argued that one can always arrange for $\bar{\lambda}_{\min}$ to be sufficiently positive to allow σ_ϵ to be sufficiently large to represent wide variations. Hence it appears that (3.1) may be a suitable specification, at least as a first approximation, for the problem of allowing variable levels of concern among voters for issues of policy.

4. Variable Levels of Concern and the Power of the Mean

Given the specification of the loss function (2.1) and the representation (3.1) of the matrix A, attention is now centered on the problem of determining the power of the vector μ_x of the means of the distribution $f_x(x)$ of the preferred points of the voters in the population. Specifically, it is shown that, at least under certain conditions, the mean vector μ_x is very powerful indeed. When the number of issues is large, it retains most of the importance which it was demonstrated to have for the case of a fixed A common to all voters.

Consider the case of competition between two candidates in an election. Let these two candidates, who are denoted by "one" and "two," have the respective platforms θ_1 and θ_2. Let the loss functions of individual voters be specified by (2.1) and the matrix A by (3.1). The components ϵ_{ij} of the matrix ϵ in (3.1) are assumed to be independently distributed with mean zero, finite variance σ_ϵ^2, whose square root satisfies (3.16), and with uniformly bounded absolute third and fourth moments. Also, ϵ and x are assumed to be independent. The nonstochastic matrix $\bar{A}$ in (3.1) is assumed to be positive definite. In addition, a further restriction, not previously discussed, must be placed on the variance-covariance matrix Σ of the distribution $f_x(x)$. Let σ_{ij} represent the component of the ith row and j^{th} column of Σ. It is assumed that

$$(4.1) \qquad \sigma_{ij} = 0 \text{ for } |i - j| > m \text{ where } m < n$$

and n represents the number of rows and columns in Σ (as well as the number of components of the vectors x, and so forth). This restriction (4.1) is not particularly serious. It means that issues exist for which, across the population, there is a zero correlation of desires. In other words, preferences are independent for certain pairs of issues. Given that such issues exist, one can always renumber the issues (since the numbering is arbitrary) and make the appropriate adjustments for (4.1) to be satisfied.

Given that the platforms θ_1 and θ_2 are announced before the election and known to all voters, the rules for the voters' choices of candidates can be specified to be the same as those used in our recent paper. Briefly, a voter casts his ballot for the first candidate if (subscripts are omitted for convenience)

(4.2) $$\|x - \theta_1\|_A^2 < \|x - \theta_2\|_A^2$$

and selects the second candidate if

(4.3) $$\|x - \theta_1\|_A^2 > \|x - \theta_2\|_A^2 .$$

In other words, a voter casts his ballot for that candidate whose platform gives him the smallest utility loss. Since it is assumed that the distribution $f_x(x)$ is normal, and thus continuous, there is no loss of generality from ignoring the possibility of some voter's obtaining equal losses from the platforms of the two candidates.

Imagine selecting a voter at random from the population $f_x(x)$. Then the probability R that such a person will vote for the first candidate instead of the second one is given by the expression

(4.4) $$R = P\left(\|x - \theta_1\|_A^2 < \|x - \theta_2\|_A^2\right)$$

which follows from (4.2) and the fact that both x and A are stochastic. Recall that the random vector x of preferred points has a marginal multivariate normal distribution with mean vector μ_x and variance-covariance matrix Σ and that x is assumed to be independent of the random matrix A.

Conditioning on the random components of A, one can write (4.4) in the following form:

(4.5) $$R = E_A\left[P(\|x - \theta_1\|_A^2 < \|x - \theta_2\|_A^2 \,|A)\right]$$

where

(4.6) $$P\left(\|x - \theta_1\|_A^2 < \|x - \theta_2\|_A^2 \,|A\right)$$

is the conditional probability that some randomly selected individual with the fixed loss matrix A votes for the first candidate.[8] Then in (4.5) the expectation is taken with respect to n^2-dimensional marginal distribution of the components of the stochastic loss matrix A. In other words, one takes the expectation in (4.5) by integrating out all the individual loss matrices.

It should be observed that expressing (4.4) in the equivalent form (4.5) allows an important alteration in the interpretation of the proba-

---

[8] For a discussion of conditional expectation such as that indicated in (4.5), see S. S. Wilks, *Mathematical Statistics* (New York: Wiley, 1962), chap. iii.

bility R. Whereas in (4.4) R could only be interpreted as the probability that a voter selected at random from the population $f_x(x)$ of preferred points would vote for the first candidate, the equivalent expression (4.5) shows that this probability can be given the interpretation of the proportion of the total vote going to the first candidate since it is implicitly assumed here that there are no abstentions. Hence it is of obvious interest to determine whether R is less than, equal to, or greater than one-half.

By the results given in Section 3 of our previous paper, since x has a marginal normal distribution, the conditional probability (4.6) is given by

(4.7) $$P\left(\|x - \theta_1\|_A^2 < \|x - \theta_2\|_A^2 \,|A\right) = \Phi[t(A)]$$

where

(4.8) $$t(A) = \frac{\|\theta_2 - \mu_x\|_A^2 - \|\theta_1 - \mu_x\|_A^2}{2\|\theta_1 - \theta_2\|_{A\ddagger A}}$$

and

(4.9) $$\Phi(t) = \int_{-\infty}^{t} \frac{1}{\sqrt{2\pi}} e^{-s^2/2} \, ds$$

so that $\Phi(t)$ is the cumulative distribution function of a unit normal variate. From (4.7) and (4.6), (4.5) can be written

(4.10) $$R = E_A\{\Phi[t(A)]\}$$

with t being the indicated function of A. Note that the expectation is still taken with respect to A. Consider the transformation

(4.11) $$t = t(A)$$

and

(4.12) $\qquad b_{ij} = a_{ij}$ for $2 \leq i \leq n$ or $2 \leq j \leq n$

where a_{ij} represents the component in the ith row and the jth column of A. Thus (4.11) and (4.12) represent a transformation from the n^2 random variables $A = \{a_{ij}\}$ to the n^2 random variables $\{t, b_{ij}\}$. From this transformation it is easily seen that (4.10) can be written

(4.13) $$R = E_t[\Phi(t)]$$

where the expectation is taken with respect to the marginal distribution of t.

The fact that t is a random variable, and has a distribution, is easily observed from (4.11) and (4.8). Let the marginal distribution of t be given by $f_t(t)$ and let $F_t(t)$ represent the corresponding cumulative distribution function. Then the right-hand side of (4.13) can be written in the equivalent form

(4.14) $$\int \Phi(t) f_t(t)\ dt = \int \Phi(t)\ dF_t(t)$$

where the right-hand side of (4.14) represents nothing more than the introduction of the notation of the Stieltjes integral. Using integration by parts on (4.14), (4.13) can be written in the form

(4.15) $$R = 1 - \int F_t(t)\ d\Phi(t).$$

Without trying to determine the actual form of the distribution $f_t(t)$ at this point in the analysis (an approximate distribution of t is derived later), let it be assumed that $f_t(t)$ is a *normal distribution* with a mean μ_t and a finite variance σ_t^2. Accordingly, $F_t(t)$ is the cumulative distribution function, that is,

(4.16) $$F_t(t) = \int_{-\infty}^{t} \frac{1}{\sqrt{2\pi}\sigma_t} e^{-\frac{1}{2\sigma_t^2}(z-\mu_t)^2}\ dz.$$

Also define $F_0(t)$ to be the cumulative distribution function of a normal variate with mean zero and finite variance σ_0^2. That is,

(4.17) $$F_0(t) = \int_{-\infty}^{t} \frac{1}{\sqrt{2\pi}\sigma_0} e^{-z^2/2\sigma_0^2}\ dz.$$

Assume that the mean μ_t of $f_t(t)$ is positive. In other terms, $\mu_t > 0$. Then it follows from (4.16) and (4.17) that, for any given value of t,

(4.18) $$F_t(t) < F_0(t)$$

so that

(4.19) $$\int F_t(t)\ d\Phi(t) < \int F_0(t)\ d\Phi(t)$$

is obviously true. It is, however, possible to write $F_0(t)$ in the following form:

(4.20) $$F_0(t) = \frac{1}{2} + g(t)$$

where $g(t)$ is an odd function. Put another way, for any t

(4.21) $$g(-t) = -g(t)$$

and

(4.22) $$g(0) = 0.$$

In other words, $g(t)$ is a translation or lowering of $F_0(t)$ so that it passes through the origin. From (4.20), the right-hand side of (4.19) can be written

$$(4.23) \quad \textstyle\int F_0(t) \, d\Phi(t) = \frac{1}{2} \int d\Phi(t) + \int g(t) \, d\Phi(t) = \frac{1}{2} + \int g(t) \, d\Phi(t);$$

hence from (4.21) and the fact that $d\Phi(t)$ is a normal distribution with mean zero and unit variance, it follows that

$$(4.24) \qquad\qquad\qquad \textstyle\int g(t) \, d\Phi(t) = 0.$$

Then from (4.24) and (4.23)

$$(4.25) \qquad\qquad\qquad \textstyle\int F_0(t) \, d\Phi(t) = \frac{1}{2}$$

follows immediately. By substitution of (4.25) into (4.19)

$$(4.26) \qquad\qquad\qquad \textstyle\int F_t(t) \, d\Phi(t) < \frac{1}{2}$$

is seen to be true. Note that (4.26) implies from (4.15) that $R > \frac{1}{2}$.

Assume now that μ_t is negative ($\mu_t < 0$). Then by an argument similar to that above

$$(4.27) \qquad\qquad\qquad \textstyle\int F_t(t) \, d\Phi(t) > \frac{1}{2}$$

is obviously true. Note that (4.27), when applied to (4.15), implies $R < \frac{1}{2}$.

The following lemma is now established:

Lemma 1: Given the previous assumptions, if the distribution $f_t(t)$ of the random variable t is normal with mean μ_t and finite variance σ_t^2, then

$$R > \tfrac{1}{2} \text{ if } \mu_t > 0$$
$$R = \tfrac{1}{2} \text{ if } \mu_t = 0$$
$$R < \tfrac{1}{2} \text{ if } \mu_t < 0.$$

Since R is defined as the proportion of the vote going to the first candidate, Lemma 1 indicates the conditions under which the first or second candidate will win the election if it can be assumed that the random variate t has a normal distribution. Hence the determination of the form of the distribution $f_t(t)$ is of obvious interest. Unfortunately, it is extremely difficult to determine the exact form of this distribution. If n, the number of issues considered by the population, is large, then the central limit theorem can be applied to give a normal approximation to $f_t(t)$. The following lemma is discussed in detail in the Appendix:

Lemma 2: For a large n, $f_t(t)$ is approximately a normal density with a finite variance and a mean

$$\mu_t = \frac{\|\theta_2 - \mu_x\|_{\bar{A}}^2 - \|\theta_1 - \mu_x\|_{\bar{A}}^2}{2n\sqrt{\beta}}$$

where β is a positive number. As $n \to \infty$ the approximation becomes more and more exact.

It is clear from Lemma 2 that the sign of μ_t, the mean of f_t using the normal approximation, is simply the sign of $\|\theta_2 - \mu_x\|_{\bar{A}} - \|\theta_1 - \mu_x\|_{\bar{A}}$. This establishes the following theorem by a straightforward application of Lemma 1:

Theorem 1: For large n,

$$
\begin{aligned}
R > \tfrac{1}{2} \text{ if } \|\theta_2 - \mu_x\|_{\bar{A}} &> \|\theta_1 - \mu_x\|_{\bar{A}} \\
R = \tfrac{1}{2} \text{ if } \|\theta_2 - \mu_x\|_{\bar{A}} &= \|\theta_1 - \mu_x\|_{\bar{A}} \\
R < \tfrac{1}{2} \text{ if } \|\theta_2 - \mu_x\|_{\bar{A}} &< \|\theta_1 - \mu_x\|_{\bar{A}}.
\end{aligned}
$$

Recall that R is interpreted as the proportion of the vote going to the first candidate. It is obvious from the theorem that, even with the specified variable levels of concern, the strategy of selecting the mean μ_x of the preferences for a political platform is dominant if the number of issues is large. If, for example, the first candidate selects $\theta_1 = \mu_x$ and the second candidate chooses $\theta_2 \neq \mu_x$, then the first inequality of the theorem holds, so that the first candidate will win the election. Obviously, the reverse is also true.

However, Theorem 1 indicates more than the mere dominance of the mean. The candidate whose platform is *closest to the mean*, with respect to the average loss matrix $\bar{A}$, wins the election.

In a sense, Theorem 1 is extremely powerful. It indicates that with a large number of issues, some of which may not even be discussed in the campaign if the candidates adopt the same stand on them, the fact that differing voters vary in respect to their concern for the various issues is irrelevant. The best advice that one can give a candidate who desires to win is that he design his platform to be the average of what the voters desire. With a large number of issues, such a platform will approximate the best one if the distribution of preferred points is approximately normal.

5. On Finding the Mean with Minimal Information

Given the importance of the mean μ_x, one may wonder whether candidates try to find it and incorporate it into their platforms. Even more important, if candidates desire to find the mean, is it possible for them to do so? In a single dimension the answer to this question obviously seems to be affirmative. Even if there were no modern surveys and pollsters, which certainly are sources of no small amount of information concerning the policy preferences of the electorate, in a single dimension with static preferences the losing candidate (his successor or his party) could always move his (or its) platform toward the winner's platform. Thus by successive iterations, with the winner staying fixed, the loser would eventually win either before or after passing over his opponent's platform (depending on initial positions). In any event, it is clear in the limit that in a single dimension such successive adjustments would converge to the dominant position.

In an n-dimensional space the answer is not so obvious. Of course, the polls contain helpful information. Yet one may wonder whether, if only the percentages of the votes are known, there exists even a theoretical method of finding the mean. The purpose of this section is to demonstrate that one such method does exist, at least under certain conditions. Given the unrealistically severe limitations on information, the existence of such a method adds plausibility to the belief that politicians in the real world can at least approximate the mean if they desire to do so.

Considering the results of the previous section, let the assumption that A is given by (3.1) be dropped and the alternative assumption be adopted that A is a symmetric, positive definite matrix of rank n. Also assume that the distribution of preferred points $f_x(x)$ is a *multivariate normal*. Let θ_1 and θ_2, with $\theta_1 \neq \theta_2$, represent the initial platforms of the two candidates. Assume that (4.2) and (4.3) are the voting rules.

The basic idea is to allow the candidates to search for a dominant position on a line in n-dimensional space, then along another line, until the over-all dominant position (the mean) is located. Consider the line

$$(5.1) \qquad \theta_\alpha = \alpha\theta_1 + (1 - \alpha)\theta_2$$

where α is any scalar. In other words, the candidates search along the line which is some linear combination of the initial positions. If a dominant position on the line exists, it is assumed that the candidates will find it in successive iterations such as were outlined above, since this problem is exactly a single-dimensional search.

It is now shown that a dominant position does exist on the line when the search is restricted to the line. Subtracting the mean from both sides of (5.1) gives

$$(5.2) \qquad \theta_\alpha - \mu_x = \alpha(\theta_1 - \theta_2) + (\theta_2 - \mu_x)$$

and taking the norm with respect to the matrix A yields

(5.3) $\quad \|\theta_\alpha - \mu_x\|^2 = \alpha^2\|\theta_1 - \theta_2\|^2 + 2\alpha(\theta_1 - \theta_2, \theta_2 - \mu_x) + \|\theta_2 - \mu_x\|^2$

where the A subscript on the norms is omitted for convenience since all the norms in this section are with respect to A.[9] Given the assumptions, a dominant position is a platform which *minimizes the "distance" from the mean.* Taking the derivative of (5.3) and setting the result to zero give

(5.4) $\quad \dfrac{d}{d\alpha}\|\theta_\alpha - \mu_x\|^2 = 2\alpha\|\theta_1 - \theta_2\|^2 + 2(\theta_1 - \theta_2, \theta_2 - \mu_x) = 0$

and solving for α yields

(5.5) $$\alpha^* = -\frac{(\theta_1 - \theta_2, \theta_2 - \mu_x)}{\|\theta_1 - \theta_2\|^2}$$

where α^* represents the particular value of α. Note that since the second derivative is positive, a minimum is attained. Also note that the minimum is unique. Let θ^* denote the platform

(5.6) $$\theta^* = \alpha^*\theta_1 + (1 - \alpha^*)\theta_2$$

and note that since α^* minimizes (5.3)

(5.7) $$\|\theta^* - \mu_x\|^2 < \|\theta_\alpha - \mu_x\|^2 \text{ for } \theta_\alpha \neq \theta^*$$

so that θ^* is dominant on the line (5.1). Obviously, if μ_x is on the line (5.1), then $\theta^* = \mu_x$. For the purpose of argument, assume that μ_x is not on the line. Also assume that one of the candidates, say the first, finds θ^* and that the second realizes that fact.

Note that (5.1) is a one-dimensional subspace of the n-dimensional space. Observe that the vector $(\theta_1 - \theta_2)$ is parallel to (5.1). Consider the subspace S defined by

(5.8) $$(\bar\theta, \theta_1 - \theta_2) = 0.$$

Subtract μ_x from both sides of (5.6) to obtain

(5.9) $$\theta^* - \mu_x = \alpha^*(\theta_1 - \theta_2) + (\theta_2 - \mu_x)$$

and observe that

(5.10) $\quad (\theta^* - \mu_x, \theta_1 - \theta_2) = \alpha^*\|\theta_1 - \theta_2\|^2 + (\theta_1 - \theta_2, \theta_2 - \mu_x) = 0$

upon substituting for α^* from (5.5). Thus the vectors $(\theta^* - \mu_x)$ and $(\theta_1 - \theta_2)$ are orthogonal. The n-1-dimensional subspace S, defined by (5.8), contains $(\theta^* - \mu_x)$ and is the orthogonal complement of $(\theta_1 - \theta_2)$. Let the second candidate select some platform θ_2^* such that

(5.11) $$\theta_2^* = \theta^* - \bar\theta$$

[9] Also note that in this notation $(\theta_1 - \theta_2, \theta_2 - \mu_x) = (\theta_1 - \theta_2)'A(\theta_2 - \mu_x)$.

where $\bar{\theta}$ is any particular vector satisfying (5.8). Now let the candidates search along the line

(5.12) $$\theta_\beta = \beta\theta^* + (1 - \beta)\theta_2^*$$

for another dominant platform where β is any scalar.

The foregoing argument is repeated again and again, with the relevant subspace losing one dimension with each repetition, until the mean μ_x is found. It should be noted that μ_x may be found either before or after the relevant subspace has been reduced to one dimension. It is clear, however, that with the relevant subspace being reduced by a dimension on each repetition, the process must converge. Obviously, at least one method exists for finding the mean when nothing more than the percentages of the votes are observed. This argument helps support the notion that, with the additional information available to candidates in the real world, they should be able at least to approximate the mean if they so desire.

6. Concluding Comments

It may be useful to state briefly the major conclusions of this paper. First, if the formulation of the phenomenon of differences between voters in their concern with various issues of policy is accepted, and if the other assumptions also are accepted, then the vector of the means of the preferred points retains its importance in the competition between two candidates within a single population which can be represented by a multivariate normal distribution. The implication seems to be that one should not worry greatly over the fact that some voters are very concerned with certain policies while others are not. If one were advising a politician in an election, it appears that there would be much to be said for telling him to find out what the voters want and to adopt a platform that is the average of those desires. The previous section argues, in a somewhat backhanded manner, that the politician should be able to follow such advice if he is motivated to do so.

Appendix

Lemma 2 gives a normal approximation to the density $f_t(t)$. Attention is now turned to finding such an approximation.

In order to simplify the notation, it is appropriate to introduce an additional assumption. Presume that $\mu_x = 0$. This assumption does not affect the analysis and therefore does not cause a loss of generality.

Given this assumption, it is easily seen from (4.11) and (4.8) that one may write

(A.1)
$$2t = \frac{\theta_2' A \theta_2 - \theta_1' A \theta_1}{\sqrt{(\theta_1 - \theta_2)' A \hat{\Sigma} A (\theta_1 - \theta_2)}}$$

and that by making the following definitions

(A.2)
$$\delta = \theta_2 - \theta_1$$
$$\delta^* = \theta_2 + \theta_1$$

one may write (A.1) in a simpler form:

(A.3)
$$2t = \frac{\delta' A \, \delta^*}{\sqrt{\delta A \hat{\Sigma} A \, \delta}}$$

which is useful for analysis. This expression (A.3) will be examined in great detail in order to determine an approximate distribution for the random variable t.

Let the number of issues expand in such a manner that all the previous assumptions are satisfied. Then investigations are made of the asymptotic distributions of the numerator and denominator of (A.3) as $n \rightarrow \infty$. Of course, an additional assumption is needed concerning the bounds of the vectors δ and δ^*.

Let δ_i and δ_i^* represent respectively the ith component of the vectors δ and δ^*. In other words, δ_i represents the difference between the first and second candidate's platforms in regard to the index measuring the ith issue. Similarly, δ_i^* represents the sum of the ith policy index in the two platforms. Assume that there exist bounds B and M, both positive, such that for all but a finite number of issues $i = 1, 2, \ldots$

(A.4)
$$|\delta_i| < B \qquad |\delta_i^*| < B$$
$$|\delta_i| > M \qquad |\delta_i^*| > M.$$

These bounds (A.5) mean that on all but a finite number of issues the candidates do not adopt the same policy position and that these positions are such that the indexes measuring the policies are finite numbers with a uniform upper bound.

The numerator of (A.3) is examined first. Given the definition (3.1) of the matrix A, it is easily seen that

(A.5)
$$\delta' A \, \delta^* = \delta' \bar{A} \, \delta^* + \delta' \, \epsilon \, \delta^*$$

and the last term on the right-hand side of (A.5) may be written

(A.6)
$$\delta' \epsilon \delta^* = \sum_i \sum_j \delta_i \, \delta_j^* \, \epsilon_{ij}.$$

Given assumption (3.2), expression (A.6) has mean zero since for all i and j in the sum

(A.7) $$E[\delta_i \, \delta_j^* \, \epsilon_{ij}] = \delta_i \, \delta_j^* \, E(\epsilon_{ij}) = 0$$

so that

(A.8) $$E[\delta'A\delta^*] = \delta\bar{A}\delta^*,$$

which is the mean of (A.5).

It is also of interest to determine the variance of (A.5). Since for independent variates the variance of a sum is the sum of the variances; consider

(A.9) $$\text{Var} \, [\delta_i \, \delta_j^* \, \epsilon_{ij}] = \delta_i^2 \, \delta_j^{*2} \, E(\epsilon_{ij}^2) = \sigma_\epsilon^2 \, \delta_i^2 \, \delta_j^{*2}$$

since $E(\epsilon_{ij}^2) = \sigma_\epsilon^2$ by assumption. Hence, from (A.9) and (A.7)

(A.10) $$\text{Var} \, [\delta'A\delta^*] = \text{Var} \, [\delta' \, \epsilon\delta^*] = \sigma_\epsilon^2 \left(\sum_i \delta_i^2 \right)\left(\sum_j \delta_j^{*2} \right).$$

But now observe that from assumption (A.4)

$$nM^2 \leq \sum_i \delta_i^2 \leq nB^2$$

(A.11)

$$nM^2 \leq \sum_j \delta_j^{*2} \leq nB^2$$

so that from (A.10) and (A.11)

(A.12) $$0 < n^2M^4 \leq \text{Var} \, [\delta'\epsilon\delta^*] \leq n^2B^4,$$

which gives a bound on the variance. This bound is used in the developments below.

A standard version of the central limit theorem is used here in the effort to find an approximate distribution for the numerator in (A.3).[10] This version states that if $z_1, \ldots, z_n$ are independent random variables with properties (A.13–A.16), then (A.18) obtains. Consider

(A.13) $$E(z_i) = 0 \qquad i = 1, \ldots, n$$

which states that all variates have mean zero,

(A.14) $$E(z_i^2) = \sigma_i^2 \qquad i, 1, \ldots, n$$

which means that all of the random variables have finite variances, and

(A.15) $$E(|z_i|^3) = \gamma_i^3 \qquad i = 1, \ldots, n$$

[10] See Harold Cramer, *Mathematical Methods of Statistics* (Princeton, N.J.: Princeton University Press, 1946), pp. 213–18.

which states that all variates have absolute third moments which are finite. Also consider

(A.16)
$$s_n^{-3} \sum_i \gamma_i^3 \to 0 \quad \text{as} \quad n \to \infty$$

where

(A.17)
$$s_n^2 = \text{Var}\left(\sum_i z_i\right) = \sum_i \sigma_i^2$$

since the z_i are independent. Given (A.13–A.16) and definition (A.17), this version of the central limit theorem states that

(A.18)
$$L\left\{s_n^{-1} \sum_i z_i\right\} \to N(0, 1) \quad \text{as} \quad n \to \infty$$

where L stands for the law or distribution of the random variable in the brackets $s_n^{-1} \Sigma_i z_i$ and the notation $N(0, 1)$ represents the normal distribution with mean zero and unit variance. In other words, a sum of independent random variables which are divided by the standard deviation of that sum has a distribution which approaches the unit normal as the number of variates in the sum approaches infinity if the specified conditions are satisfied. It is now necessary to determine whether these conditions can be satisfied for the problem at hand so that the central limit theorem can be applied.

It is obvious from (A.6) that the term $\delta'\epsilon\delta^*$ involves a double sum in the independent random variates $\delta_i \, \delta_j^* \, \epsilon_{ij}$. However, the double sum in (A.6) can be considered as a single sum of n^2 terms so that this condition is satisfied. Consider requirement (A.15). The third absolute moment of the i, j^{th} term in (A.6) is

(A.19) $\quad E(|\delta_i \, \delta_j^* \, \epsilon_{ij}|^3) = |\delta_i|^3 \, |\delta_j^*|^3 \, E(|\epsilon_{ij}|^3) \le B^6 \, E(|\epsilon_{ij}|^3) < B^*$

for some bound B^* since it is assumed that the third absolute moments of the ϵ_{ij} are uniformly bounded. From (A.19) it follows that

(A.20)
$$\sum_i \sum_j E(|\delta_i \, \delta_j^* \, \epsilon_{ij}|^3) \le n^2 B^*$$

since the ϵ_{ij} are assumed to be identically distributed. Define

(A.21)
$$S_n^2 = \text{Var}[\delta' \, \epsilon\delta^*]$$

so that from (A.12)

(A.22)
$$nM^2 \le S_n \le nB^2$$

and from (A.20) and (A.22)

(A.23) $$S_n^{-3} \sum_i \sum_j E(|\delta_i \, \delta_j^* \, \epsilon_{ij}|^3) \leq n^{-1} M^{-6} B^*,$$

which goes to zero as $n \to \infty$. This result (A.23) shows that condition (A.16) is satisfied. Also, (A.19) indicates that (A.15) is satisfied, and (A.14) is satisfied by assumption (3.11). The conditions for the application of the central theorem are satisfied.

A slight variation of the central limit theorem stated above is used here. Note from (A.22) that n and S_n are of the same order. Thus, dividing $\delta' \, \epsilon\delta^*$ by n instead of S_n, the application of the central limit theorem gives

(A.24) $$L\left\{ \frac{1}{n} \, \delta' \, \epsilon\delta^* \right\} \to N(0, \sigma_n^2) \quad \text{as} \quad n \to \infty$$

where

(A.25) $$M^4 \leq \sigma_n^2 \leq B^4$$

and where L stands for the law or distribution of the term inside the brackets with $N(0, \sigma_n^2)$ representing the normal distribution with zero mean and finite variance σ_n^2. Thus (A.24) gives the asymptotic distribution of the random portion of the numerator, divided by n, of (A.3). This result will be of use.

It is now appropriate to consider the denominator of (A.3). From the definition (3.1) of the matrix A

(A.26) $$\delta' A \not\!\!Z A \delta = \delta' \bar{A} \not\!\!Z \bar{A} \delta + 2\delta' \bar{A} \not\!\!Z \, \epsilon\delta + \delta' \epsilon \not\!\!Z \, \epsilon\delta$$

and the terms on the right-hand side of (A.26) will be examined in turn. Define the vector w to be

(A.27) $$w = \epsilon\delta$$

and let the ith component of w be denoted w_i. Then from (A.27)

(A.28) $$w_i = \sum_j \epsilon_{ij} \, \delta_j;$$

hence it follows that

(A.29) $$E(w_i) = 0$$

since the ϵ_{ij} have expectation zero, and

(A.30) $$E(w_i^2) = \sigma_\epsilon^2 \sum_j \delta_j^2$$

since σ_ϵ^2 is the assumed variance of the independent variates ϵ_{ij}. It also follows that the components $w_1, \ldots, w_n$ are independant random variables. With the substitution of the definition (A.27) into the middle term on the right-hand side of (A.26), define

$$(A.31) \qquad u_n = \frac{1}{n^2} \delta' \bar{A} \mathcal{Z} w.$$

Given (A.29), it is obviously true that

$$(A.32) \qquad E(u_n) = \frac{1}{n^2} \delta' \bar{A} \mathcal{Z} [E(w)] = 0.$$

By the Schwartz Inequality

$$(A.33) \qquad u_n^2 \leq \frac{1}{n^4} (\delta' \bar{A} \mathcal{Z} \delta)(w' \bar{A} \mathcal{Z} w).$$

Let it be assumed that

$$(A.34) \qquad \bar{A} \leq \mathcal{Z}^{-1},$$

which, as was explained in our recent paper, does not result in any loss of generality. The ordinal nature of utility, allowing A to be multiplied by a scalar, means that one can always arrange for (A.34) to be satisfied. Applying assumption (A.34) to (A.33) gives

$$(A.35) \qquad u_n^2 \leq \frac{1}{n^4} (\delta' \delta)(w' w);$$

whence by taking the expectation and using (A.30)

$$(A.36) \quad E(u_n^2) \leq \frac{1}{n^4} \left[\sum_i \delta_i^2 \right] \left[\sum_j E(w_j^2) \right] = \frac{\sigma_\epsilon^2}{n^4} \left(\sum_i \delta_i^2 \right)^2$$

is obtained. However, from (A.11) comes

$$(A.37) \qquad \sum_i \delta_i^2 \leq nB^2$$

so that, applying (A.37) to (A.36),

$$(A.38) \qquad E(u_n^2) \leq \frac{\sigma_\epsilon^2}{n^2} B^4$$

is obtained. Now note that (A.38) implies, given (A.32), that

$$(A.39) \qquad \text{Var}(u_n) \to 0 \text{ as } n \to \infty,$$

so that, from (A.39) and (A.32), in probability

$$(A.40) \qquad u_n \to 0 \text{ as } n \to \infty.$$

This completes the examination of the middle term on the right-hand side of (A.26).

Consider the term on the extreme right of (A.28). Dividing by n^2 and applying (A.27) give the following definition,

$$(A.41) \qquad\qquad v_n = \frac{1}{n^2}\, w' \mathfrak{L} w,$$

which must be examined. Let $\bar{\alpha}_n$ and $\underline{\alpha}_n$ represent respectively the maximum and minimum eigenvalues of $\mathfrak{L}$. Assume that there exist positive bounds $\bar{\alpha}$ and $\underline{\alpha}$ such that for all n

$$\bar{\alpha}_n \le \bar{\alpha}$$
$$(A.42)$$
$$\underline{\alpha}_n \ge \underline{\alpha} > 0.$$

Then from the properties of eigenvalues

$$(A.43) \qquad\qquad \underline{\alpha}_n \le \frac{w' \mathfrak{L} w}{w' w} \le \bar{\alpha}_n$$

so that

$$(A.44) \qquad \frac{1}{n^2}\, \underline{\alpha} \sum_i w_i^2 \le v_n \le \frac{1}{n^2}\, \bar{\alpha} \sum_i w_i^2$$

is obviously true. Taking the expectation of (A.44) and using (A.30) give

$$(A.45) \qquad \frac{\sigma_\epsilon^2}{n}\, \underline{\alpha} \sum_j \delta_j^2 \le E(v_n) \le \frac{\sigma_\epsilon^2}{n}\, \bar{\alpha} \sum_j \delta_j^2$$

so that from (A.11) comes

$$(A.46) \qquad\qquad \underline{\alpha}\sigma_\epsilon^2 M^2 \le E(v_n) \le \bar{\alpha}\sigma_\epsilon^2 B^2.$$

Recall assumption (4.1). Given this assumption, v_n can be written as a sum of random variables w_i^* where

$$(A.47) \qquad\qquad w_i^* = \sum_{|i-j| \le m} \sigma_{ij} w_i w_j$$

Hence, for some k where $k > i + 2m$, w_k^* is independent of w_i^* because it can be seen from (A.47) that the $w_i w_j$ terms in w_i^* are different from the $w_k w_r$ terms in w_k^*. Furthermore, the set of random variables $(w_a^*, \ldots , w_b^*)$ and $(w_c^*, \ldots , w_d^*)$ is independent if $c > b + 2m$. Such a sequence is called $2m$-dependent.[11] From (A.46) and the law of large numbers for m-dependent sequences, it follows that in probability

---

[11] Such sequences are discussed and the law of large numbers for m-dependent sequences is stated and proved in P. Diananda, "Some Probability Limit Theorems with Statistical Applications," *Proceedings of the Cambridge Philosophical Society,* XLIX (1953), 239–46.

(A.48) $$v_n \to \beta \text{ as } n \to \infty$$

with

(A.49) $$\sigma_\epsilon^2 \underline{\alpha} M^2 \le \beta \le \sigma_\epsilon^2 \bar{\alpha} B^2$$

so that β is some positive number. This completes the discussion of the term on the extreme right of (A.26).

The remaining term to be considered in (A.26) is $\delta' \bar{A} \pmb{\Sigma} \bar{A} \delta$. Since $\bar{A} \le \pmb{\Sigma}^{-1}$

(A.50) $$\delta' \bar{A} \pmb{\Sigma} \bar{A} \, \delta \le \delta' \pmb{\Sigma}^{-1} \delta \le \bar{\lambda}_n \, \delta' \delta$$

where $\bar{\lambda}_n$ is the maximum eigenvalue of $\pmb{\Sigma}^{-1}$. However, the maximum eigenvalue of $\pmb{\Sigma}^{-1}$ is the reciprocal of the minimum eigenvalue of $\pmb{\Sigma}$, which is bounded below by $\underline{\alpha}$, as seen in (A.42). Thus from (A.50) and (A.37)

(A.51) $$\frac{1}{n^2} \delta' \bar{A} \pmb{\Sigma} \bar{A} \delta \le \frac{nB^2}{n^2 \alpha} \le \frac{1}{n} \frac{B^2}{\alpha} \to 0$$

as $n \to \infty$.

The problem of combining the foregoing results remains. Recall that the square root of (A.26) is the denominator of (A.3). In other words,

(A.52) $$\sqrt{\delta' A \pmb{\Sigma} A \delta} = (\delta' \bar{A} \pmb{\Sigma} \bar{A} \delta + 2\delta' \bar{A} \pmb{\Sigma} w + w' \pmb{\Sigma} w)^{1/2}$$

is the denominator of (A.3) where definition (A.27) has been substituted in some of the terms. Dividing by n and substituting from (A.31) and (A.41) give

(A.53) $$\frac{1}{n} \sqrt{\delta' A \pmb{\Sigma} A \delta} = \left[\frac{1}{n^2} (\delta' \bar{A} \pmb{\Sigma} \bar{A} \delta + 2u_n + v_n) \right]^{1/2} .$$

From the application of (A.40), (A.48), and (A.51) to (A.53), it follows that in probability

(A.54) $$\frac{1}{n} \sqrt{\delta' A \pmb{\Sigma} A \delta} \to \sqrt{\beta} \quad \text{as} \quad n \to \infty .$$

Now observe that by applying definitions (A.2) to the first term on the right-hand side of (A.5), it is possible to write (A.3) in the following equivalent form upon dividing both numerator and denominator by n:

(A.55) $$2t = \frac{\dfrac{1}{n} \left(\|\theta_2\|_{\bar{A}}^2 - \|\theta_1\|_{\bar{A}}^2 \right) + \dfrac{1}{n} \delta' \, \epsilon \delta^*}{\dfrac{1}{n} \sqrt{\delta' A \pmb{\Sigma} A \delta}} .$$

Also observe that as $n \to \infty$,

(A.56) $$\frac{1}{n} \left(\|\theta_2\|_{\bar{A}}^2 - \|\theta_1\|_{\bar{A}}^2 \right) \to d$$

where d is some number. Cramer states and proves the following convergence theorem.[12] Let $z_1, \ldots, z_n$ and $y_1, \ldots, y_n$ be sequences of random variables such that as $n \to \infty$ that in probability

(A.57) $\qquad\qquad L\{z_n\} \to L\{z\}$ and $y_n \to c$

where L stands for the law or distribution and c is a constant; then

(A.58) $$L\left\{\frac{z_n}{y_n}\right\} \to L\left\{\frac{z}{c}\right\}.$$

It is obvious that Cramer's theorem has application here. As $n \to \infty$, it is clear from (A.24) and (A.56) that the numerator in (A.55) is asymptotically normal with mean d and variance σ_n^2. From (A.54), the denominator approaches a constant. Hence, dividing by 2, as $n \to \infty$

(A.59) $\qquad\qquad L\{t\} \to N(d/2\sqrt{\beta},\ \sigma_n^2/4\beta).$

Thus t is asymptotically normal with the indicated mean and variance.

It should be observed, however, that one need not let n go "all the way" to infinity. Instead, one can use the familiar corruption of the limit theorems to state from (A.59) and (A.55) that for large n

(A.60) $$f_t(t) = N\left[\frac{1}{2n\sqrt{\beta}}\left(\|\theta_2\|_{\bar{A}}^2 - \|\theta_1\|_{\bar{A}}^2\right), \frac{\sigma_n^2}{4\beta}\right]$$

so that the density of t, $f_t(t)$, is approximately normal with a mean whose sign is determined by $\|\theta_2\|_{\bar{A}}^2 - \|\theta_1\|_{\bar{A}}^2$.

---

[12] See Cramer, *op. cit.*, p. 254, where the theorem is stated in a slightly different fashion.

An Impossibility Result Concerning the Theory of Decision-Making[*]

2 Gerald H. Kramer
University of Rochester

1. Introduction

THE purpose of this study is to investigate the relationship between the theory of rational decision-making, on the one hand, and the finite information-processing capacities possessed by real decision-makers, on the other. In particular, we wish to show that the behavioral implications of the former are in a certain sense formally incompatible with the limitations on behavior imposed by the latter.

"Rationality," for present purposes, will be taken to mean simply that the decision-making agent in question behaves as though he were capable of forming consistent preferences over the set of relevant possible states of affairs and of acting in accord with these preferences. This concept of rationality seems an indispensable component, at least at some level, of any comprehensive theory of political behavior. In formal attempts at a pure theory of politics, as exemplified by the works of Arrow, Black, Downs, or Riker, the rationality premise usually is made explicit and plays a fundamental role in the analysis. Even in more informal descriptive treatments of political processes we can scarcely avoid speaking at times in terms of the interests, or aspirations, or deprivations of various agents in the system, and such terminology again suggests that we regard these agents as entities which possess definite interests or preferences, which they attempt to advance in their actions.

If the environment in which such a decision-maker must operate is sufficiently complex, his attempts to attain desired outcomes may be severely distorted, and indeed it may be necessary to extend or redefine the concept of rationality for some such situations. Such environmental complications can arise, for example, because of:

* This research was originally undertaken at the Massachusetts Institute of Technology under a grant from the Social Science Research Council and subsequently revised while the author was a guest of the Cowles Foundation for Research in Economics at Yale University.

a) limitations on the power or resources at the disposal of the decision-maker; or

b) institutional or environmental factors which make uncertain the relations between means and ends; or

c) interactions with other agents, who are pursuing their own interests.

Constraints of the first type can in principle be incorporated into the analysis by suitable restrictions upon the decision-maker's choice set. In the second case, if probabilities can be associated with the various uncertainties, the rationality concept can be readily extended to cover the type of situation, of decision-making under risk. If no such probabilities can be assigned, or if the uncertainty arises from the third type of complication—interaction with other agents—then serious conceptual and theoretical problems arise. However, these problems, which form the subject matter of the theory of decision-making under uncertainty and the theory of games, will not be considered here. For present purposes, it will suffice to consider the case of a single decision-maker in the simplest of environments, in which there is no uncertainty and in which there is a one-to-one relationship between the desired outcomes and the alternative courses of action available to the decision-maker. Hence it will not be necessary to distinguish means from ends explicitly, and we can use the term "alternatives" to refer to either without ambiguity.

There is another kind of constraint, however, arising from the limited information-processing capabilities of the decision-making agent, which poses difficulties of a more fundamental nature. Herbert Simon, especially, has argued that in many contexts the rationality premise is an unrealistic one on which to base a theory of decision-making because it fails to take into account the limited computational capacities possessed by real decision-makers.[1] Clearly, if such limitations exist and if their existence affects the ability of the agent to pursue his goals, then the viability of the theory is indeed brought into serious question, since such internal constraints are not easily reconciled with a theory of overt behavior.

That such capacity limitations do exist, and are important, is generally taken to be self-evident, or in any event easily justified on the basis of casual observation of everyday experience. For example, to reduce a game of chess to normal form (that is, to enumerate the possible strategies), which is a necessary prerequisite for any game-theoretic type of analysis, would require some fantastic number of hours on a large, high-

---

[1] See particularly H. A. Simon, *Models of Man* (New York: John Wiley & Sons, 1957), pp. 196 ff and 241 ff; also H. A. Simon, "Theories of Decision-Making in Economics and Behavioral Science," *American Economic Review*, XLIX (1959).

speed computer. Even at a more prosaic level, for a consumer to determine the "best" bundle of commodities compatible with a given budget
constraint, as he is pictured as doing by the theory of consumer behavior,
would require considerable time and expertise with a slide rule or desk
calculator, given the packaging and pricing practices which typically
prevail. Clearly the vast majority of chess players and consumers do not
and indeed cannot perform such computational feats; hence, the argument goes, the rationality premise, which implicitly assumes that they
can and do, is clearly unsatisfactory for a descriptive theory of decision-
making.

Even if we grant the validity of these empirical observations, the argument itself is not necessarily conclusive. For the validity of the theory of
decision-making does not directly depend on whether decision-makers
really have consistent preference orderings, or actually perform complicated calculations; the theory asserts only that they behave *as if* they
did. Even if real decision-makers in everyday environments cannot perform the calculations required for a comprehensive analysis of their
problems and instead rely on simple rules of thumb or other devices to
guide their choices, it may nevertheless be true that these simpler rules
lead them to behave as if they were acting rationally, at least to a reasonable approximation. The question of whether they are *really* rational
or merely act *as if* they were, is surely unimportant practically and
probably is meaningless epistemologically as well. So goes the counter-
argument.

In principle, the best way to resolve this question of the behavioral
implications of information-processing limitations would be with a carefully designed series of experiments; in practice, it has proved very difficult to design really conclusive experiments, and the empirical evidence
is ambiguous. The purpose of the present study is to approach this question in a different, more formal fashion. Specifically, a decision-maker
will be considered as some sort of finite information-processing device, or
automaton. A formal theory of such devices—the theory of finite automata [2]—will then be used to explore the question of whether such a device is *capable* of behaving rationally. Thus, we will not inquire into the
specific decision rules, or program, used by any particular automaton,
but rather, we shall consider whether there is any *conceivable* program
for such a device which could lead to input-output behavior consistent
with the theory of decision-making.

The question can be posed more formally in the following terms. A
decision-making entity behaves *rationally* just in case its behavior

[2] See, for example, M. O. Rabin and D. Scott, "Finite Automata and Their Decision Problems," *IBM Journal of Research and Development*, III (1959).

satisfies the following conditions: With respect to a given universal set $\mathfrak{U}$ of alternatives $\{a, a', a'', \ldots\}$ there is a binary relation $\geq$ (the preference-or-indifference relation) defined over $\mathfrak{U}$ and a (partial) input-output function F (the decision function), where [3] $F: \mathcal{P}(\mathfrak{U}) \to \mathfrak{U}$, which satisfy:

  i(a) For any $a, a' \epsilon \mathfrak{U}$, either $a \geq a'$ or $a' \geq a$ or both.
  (b) For any $a, a', a'' \epsilon \mathfrak{U}$, if $a \geq a'$ and $a' \geq a''$, then $a \geq a''$.
  (c) For any $A \subset \mathfrak{U}$, $F(A) \epsilon \mathcal{C}$ where $a \epsilon \mathcal{C}$ if and only if $a \epsilon A$ and $a \geq a'$ for all $a' \epsilon A$.

Schematically, the decision-maker is considered as a kind of input-output device (see Figure 2.1). The input A to the device is a set of alternatives, and the output a is some member of A which is preferred or indifferent to all other available alternatives, according to some con-

Figure 2.1. Schematic representation of a decision-maker as an input-output device

sistent preference ordering $\geq$ over the set of all possible alternatives.

Such a decision-making entity can be thought of as some sort of information-processing or generalized computing device. Suppose we now impose the additional condition, that the decision-making entity must be a *finite* computing device, which will be defined more carefully below. The question to be investigated is whether this additional condition, in conjunction with the rationality assumptions (i), leads to a contradiction; we shall show that, except for some degenerate special cases, such a contradiction does indeed arise.

2. Preliminaries

A finite computing device, or finite automaton,[4] will mean here a finite apparatus which somehow can accept or receive a symbolic input (the

---

[3] Here $\mathcal{P}(\mathfrak{U})$ is the power set, or set of all subsets, of $\mathfrak{U}$. The notation $F: A \to B$ means that F is a mapping from A into B, that is, a function with domain in A and range in B.

[4] Cf. Rabin and Scott, *op. cit.*, and J. C. Shepherdson, "The Reduction of Two-Way Automata to One-Way Automata," *IBM Journal of Research and Development*, III (1959).

problem) and can subsequently produce and communicate a symbolic output (the decision). The device may be mechanical or electrical, or it may operate on some other principle; the only requirement is that it be finite—that is, of finite extension and composed of finitely many parts, each of which can take on only finitely many distinct configurations.

The symbolic input may be regarded as being transcribed onto an arbitrarily long input tape. The tape is subdivided into spaces, and on each space an input symbol (a member of a fixed, finite input alphabet, Σ_I) is printed. The entire input is written on the tape in this fashion by means of the *input language*, to be described below.

The device itself can be thought of as composed of three major components: a tape reader, to read the input tape; an output unit, for communicating the final output; and a central computing unit, which monitors and controls the tape reader, performs the appropriate computations, and eventually communicates its output by means of the output unit. The output is printed, symbol by symbol, upon a one-way output tape, according to some fixed output language. Such a device is shown schematically in Figure 2.2.

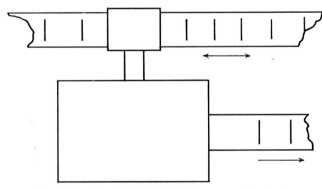

Figure 2.2. Schematic representation of a generalized finite computing device

Time is assumed to be partitioned into discrete intervals, $t = 1$, $2, \ldots$. The tape reader at any instant of time is positioned over some space on the input tape, sensing the symbol printed on that space; upon command from the computing unit it can move the input tape in either direction and stop it on some new space, whose contents it then senses and communicates to the computing unit. Thus the reader can "scan" the symbolic input in any required fashion. In order to enable the reader to anticipate the ends of the tape and thus to avoid having it run off the tape inadvertently while scanning the input, every input tape is begun with a special symbol "B" and ended with another special symbol "E," neither of these special symbols appearing elsewhere in the input. Thus an input string of k symbols will be transcribed onto an input tape $k + 2$ spaces long. The tape reader can thus avoid running off the tape by always moving the tape to the left when it encounters the "B" and to the right when it meets the "E" on all except the terminal scan.

The central computing unit is composed of some finite number μ of distinct parts, each of which can take on, say, η_i distinct configurations or positions. When each part is in a specific position, the device as a whole is in an over-all configuration, or *state;* when some part changes its configuration, then the device as a whole is in a new state. Clearly the number of distinct states is bounded by $\prod_{i=1}^{\mu} \eta_i$, and is, therefore, finite.

At any time t, the device will be in some state s, with its reader sensing some particular input symbol σ. The device may then do any or all of the following: it may produce some output; it may change its internal configuration to some new state; or it may move the input tape a number of spaces in either direction. Hence the behavior or the device can be completely described by a set of rules which specify the output, the new state, and the direction and distance that the input tape shall be moved whenever the device is in a certain state reading a certain symbol. Without loss of generality the outputs can be thought of as being produced one symbol at a time, and the input tape can be permitted to move only one square at a time. Let S be the set of all states and let Σ_I and Σ_0 be the input and output alphabets, respectively. As noted above, Σ_I is augmented with the special symbols "B" and "E" to mark the beginnings and ends of tapes. The device must also be able to perform a part of its computation without giving any output, so Σ_0 is augmented with another special symbol "e," such that whenever the computing unit specifies adding an "e" to the output, this leaves the output unchanged—i.e., amounts to giving no output. The rules which describe the operation of the device must specify, for each state s and input symbol σ for which the device does not "jam," a new state s', an output symbol σ', and an integer $m \in \{-1, 0, +1\}$, the latter meaning that the input tape shall be moved m spaces to the left (where $m = -1$ means 1 space to the right). Abstractly these rules can be represented by a finite set Q of *quintuples*, of the form $(s, \sigma, s', \sigma', m)$. To characterize the behavior of the device completely, the beginning and end of its computation must be described. A certain number s_0 of S is designated as the *initial state;* the computation is begun with the device in s_0 reading the initial "B" of the input tape. If there is a quintuple beginning with s_0, B then the device goes into the new state, gives the output, and moves the input tape as specified by that quintuple. If $m = 1$ in that quintuple, the device is now in a state s' reading the initial symbol of the input string, and it now invokes a new quintuple. The device continues to operate in this manner until one of four things happens: it may eventually run off the tape to the right; it may run off to the left; it may enter a state s reading a symbol σ such that there is no quintuple beginning with s, σ, in which case it simply halts or "jams"; or, finally, it may go into an infinite "loop" and keep computing forever. For any string x of symbols in the input alphabet, the device will be said to *accept* the string x (or the input tape BxE) just in case, when the device is begun in s_0 reading the "B" of the input tape BxE, it eventually does the first of these—that is, runs off the right end of the tape. If the device accepts x and produces a string y of output symbols (possibly the null string, Λ) while doing so, then y is an *output*, and the device *maps x into y.* The input-output behavior of the device can be summarized with a function G, defined by

$G(x) = y$ if and only if the device maps x into y; not defined otherwise.

Hence the domain of G is the set of all acceptable inputs, and its range is the set of possible outputs.

The input and output languages must also be described more precisely. A language, generally, can be characterized as a system (Σ, R_1, R_2), where Σ is a fixed, finite set of symbols (the alphabet); R_1 is a finite set of syntactic rules (the grammar), which govern the manner in which symbols can be combined into well-formed strings ("sentences"); and R_2 is a set of semantic rules governing the use ("meaning") of various well-formed strings.[5] In the case of a natural language, for example English, Σ might be the set of morphemes of English, R_1 a syntax or grammar of English, and R_2 a semantic theory of English. As an example of a formal language, take the usual notation of the theory of consumer behavior, where commodity bundles are represented by n-tuples of numbers $(x_1, x_2, \ldots, x_n)$. Let $\Sigma = \{1, 2, \ldots, 9, 0, ,, (,)\}$, and let R_1 be a set of simple recursive rules specifying how to combine digits to form numerals and how to combine numerals, commas, and parentheses to represent sets of n-tuples. Finally, R_2 would specify that the string representing an n-tuple $(x_1, x_2, \ldots, x_n)$ be interpreted as a commodity bundle of x_1 units of some designated first commodity, x_2 units of the second commodity, and so on.

For present purposes it will not be necessary to inquire in detail into

---

[5] See, for example, Noam Chomsky, *Syntactic Structures* (The Hague: Mouton, 1957); also G. K. Krulee *et al.*, "Natural Language Inputs for a Problem-solving System," *Behavioral Science*, IX (1964).

the structures of the particular input and output languages used by the device. It will, however, be necessary to place certain restrictions on these languages to ensure that the decision problem is not "solved" by simply transforming it into a linguistic problem. With respect to the input language L_I, for example, clearly the alternatives should not be presented to the device in a manner dependent upon their relative values; just as, in the case of experimentation with a decision-maker, the physical arrangement of the alternatives should not reveal the solution. Hence the input language L_I must satisfy the following condition, with respect to a given universal set $\mathcal{U}$ of alternatives:

ii(a) Every finite set A of alternatives must be representable by a well-formed string.

   (b) Every well-formed string must represent one and only one set.

   (c) There exist substrings w, y, z, and for every finite set A_i of alternatives there exists a substring x_i, such that the string $wx_{i_1}yx_{i_2}yx_{i_3} \ldots x_{i_k}z$ represents $A_{i_1} \cup A_{i_2} \cup \ldots \cup A_{i_k}, k > 1$.

The first condition ensures that L_I will be rich enough to describe any finite set, while the second specifies that the descriptions shall be unambiguous. The third condition in effect requires that sets be describable by lists, where the order of listing is inessential. Thus, suppose that A_1 is the set composed of objects a and b, while A_2 consists of object c; if we let w be the symbol {, y be ,, z be }, and let x_1 and x_2 be **a, b** and **c**, then the usual notation of elementary set theory clearly satisfies (ii, c), since the union of A_1 and A_2 is represented by **{a, b, c}** or by **{c, a, b}**. This listing condition is also satisfied by English, by means of the commutative connectors "and" and "or," and it clearly is also satisfied by most other natural and formal languages of interest.

Trivial solutions can also arise from the choice of an output language. For example, the verbal responses "I choose alternative a_3" and "I choose that alternative which maximizes my utility" may in fact denote the same thing, but in the second case the computational burden of identifying the alternative in question is simply passed on to whoever must decode the device's output. This problem can be avoided by requiring that the choices be indicated in a uniform manner; more precisely, L_0 must satisfy:

iii(a) Every alternative shall be representable by some well-formed output string.

   (b) Distinct well-formed output strings y, y' shall represent distinct alternatives a, a'.

Hence the correspondence between output strings and alternatives must be one-to-one.

A final degenerate type of solution that should be excluded is one arising from a trivial universal set of alternatives or from a trivial preference structure. If the number of possible alternatives is limited, it would be possible in principle for a sufficiently large finite device (large relative to the number of alternatives) simply to memorize them and to behave consistently in this uninteresting way; hence the number of possible alternatives will be assumed to be infinite. It will suffice for our purposes to consider a denumerably infinite universal set $\mathcal{U}$ of alternatives (that is, a set whose members can be put into a one-to-one correspondence with the positive integers). Another uninteresting situation is where the decision-maker is indifferent to all the alternatives, or where he has only a limited number of categories of preference; to avoid these situations, the number of preference categories will also be required to be (denumerably) infinite. More formally, the relation of indifference, $\sim$, which is an equivalence relation defined by $a \sim a'$ if and only if $a \gtrsim a'$ and also $a' \gtrsim a$, is assumed to be of infinite index.

3. Proof of the Result

With respect to a given automaton, the set of all input tapes can be partitioned into finitely many classes T_1, T_2, . . . T_m, such that the members of each class are equivalent with respect to the transitions they produce in the device. More precisely, for any tape x, define the function[6]

$$\tau_x \text{ (where } \tau_x \colon S \times \{-1, +1\} \to [S \times \{-1, +1\}] \cup \{0\})$$

as follows: to find $\tau_x(s, -1)$ put the device in state s reading the leftmost symbol of x and let it begin computing. If it eventually runs off x to the right, in state s', then set $\tau_x(s, -1) = (s', +1)$; if it exits to the left in s'', set $\tau_x(s, -1) = (s'', -1)$; and if it does neither (that is, jams or goes into an infinite loop), then set $\tau_x(s, -1) = 0$. We obtain $\tau_x(s, +1)$ similarly, beginning the device on the rightmost symbol of x. Thus τ_x summarizes the transitional behavior of the device with respect to the tape x, and such a function is defined (and is effectively computable) for each possible input tape. However, each such function has the same finite domain, $S \times \{-1, +1\}$, and its range must be a subset of the same finite set, $[S \times \{-1, +1\}] \cup \{0\}$. Hence, only finitely many distinct τ_x are possible (at most $(2n + 1)^{2n}$, where n is the number of states), and the set of

[6] Cf. Shepherdson, *op. cit.* The cross product $A \times B$ denotes the set of all ordered pairs $<a, b>$ where $a \in A$ and $b \in B$.

input tapes can therefore be partitioned into finitely many classes that are equivalent with respect to the transition function τ_x.

For any output string x, let $\lambda(x)$ be defined as the number of symbols in the string. We now wish to establish the following proposition, which relates an input tape $Bx_1x_2 \ldots x_kE$ to the length of the resulting output string $G(x_1x_2 \ldots x_k)$:

> iv With respect to the automaton (S, s_0, Q) with associated equivalence classes $T_1, T_2, \ldots, T_m$, let $p_1, p_2, \ldots, p_k$ be a finite sequence of integers such that $1 \leq p_i \leq m$. Form an input tape $Bx_1x_2 \ldots x_kE$, such that the ith segment x_i is a member of the $p_i{}^{th}$ class, T_{p_i}. Then either:
>
> (a) the device will fail to accept any such tape or else
>
> (b) the device will accept every such tape, and moreover there exists a sequence of functions $f_1, f_2, \ldots, f_k$ (where $f_i: T_{p_i} \rightarrow \{0, 1, 2, \ldots\}$) such that $\lambda(G(x_1x_2 \ldots x_k)) = \sum_{i=1}^{k} f_i(x_i)$ for each such tape.

More informally, from any tape accepted by the device a new tape can be formed, by segmenting the original tape in any fashion and then changing some or all segments by substituting another member of the same equivalence class. Part (b) of the proposition assures us that this new tape will also be accepted and that the effect (upon the length of the resulting output) of each substitution can be measured independently.

To establish the proposition, note that from the definition of τ, if $\tau_y = \tau_{y'}$ then $\tau_{wyz} = \tau_{wy'z}$. Thus, in particular, let w be $Bx_1x_2 \ldots x_{i-1}$ and z be $x_{i+1} \ldots x_kE$, and let x_i' be from the same class T_{p_i} as x_i; then $\tau_{wx_iz}(s_0, -1) = \tau_{wx_i'z}(s_0, -1)$, and either both tapes are rejected or both are accepted. This establishes (a) and the initial part of (b). To establish the remainder of (b), consider the movement of the reading head across the boundary between wx_i and z. It will cross first to the right, then to the left, and so on until the computation terminates. Let $s_{r_1}, s_{l_1}, s_{r_2}, s_{l_2}, \ldots, s_{r_k}$ be the sequence of states the device is in after each successive crossing. Clearly the output produced during the ith passage through z is completely determined by the state s_{r_i} at the beginning of the passage and by the segment z itself and does not depend on wx_i directly. The foregoing sequence of states is defined by the recursive conditions:

1)
$$\tau_{wx_i}(s_0, -1) = (s_{r_1}, +1)$$

2)
$$\tau_z(s_{r_i}, -1) = (s_{1_i}, -1), \quad i < k$$
$$= (s', +1), \quad i = k$$

3)
$$\tau_{wx_i}(s_{1_i}, +1) = (s_{r_{i+1}}, +1), \quad i \leq k.$$

If we now substitute another segment x_i' for x_i, such that $\tau_{x_i'} = \tau_{x_i}$, then (2) is obviously unaffected, and since $\tau_{wx_i} = \tau_{wx_i'}$, as noted above, conditions (1) and (3) are also unaffected. Hence the sequence of states, and therefore the amount of output produced by the device while scanning the segment z, is unchanged by such a substitution. By an analogous argument, the amount of output produced while scanning w is also unchanged, and the only effect of the substitution is in the output produced during the actual scanning of the substituted segment, x_i'. Thus, if $f_i(x_i')$ is defined as the amount of output produced during the scanning of x_i', for any $x_i' \,\epsilon\, T_{p_i}$, $i = 1, \ldots, k$, then the remainder of (b) follows immediately.

We now return, finally, to the original question of whether a finite device is capable of behaving rationally. An input-output device which behaves rationally must satisfy conditions (i), (ii), and (iii), while a finite device must satisfy (iv). It will now be shown that these two sets of restrictions are inconsistent, and hence that a finite device satisfying proposition (iv) is indeed incapable of also satisfying the rationality conditions.

Let $A = \{a, a', a'', \ldots\}$ be a denumerably infinite set of alternatives such that no two of them are indifferent. The earlier assumptions concerning the universal set $\mathfrak{U}$ and the preference ordering $\geq$, in Section 2, guarantee the existence of such a set. From condition (ii, c) on the input language for each member a of A there must exist a substring x which represents the singleton set $\{a\}$. Hence corresponding to A there is an infinite set $X = \{x, x', x'', \ldots\}$ of substrings.

If the decision-making device is finite, it has associated with it the equivalence classes $T_1, T_2, \ldots, T_m$. If the set X of substrings is partitioned into these classes, clearly at least one of the equivalence classes will contain infinitely many members of X. Let $X^* = \{x_1, x_2, \ldots, x_i, \ldots\}$ be this infinite subset of X, and let $A^* = \{a_1, a_2, \ldots, a_i, \ldots\}$ be the corresponding set of alternatives, where x_i corresponds to $\{a_i\}$ for all i.

Let a_i and a_j be any two distinct members of A^*. Since no two members of A (and therefore of A^*) are indifferent, one of these two must be strictly preferred to the other; let us suppose that a_j is the preferred one. From condition (ii, c), there exist substrings w, y, z such that wx_iyx_jz and wx_jyx_iz both represent $\{a_i\} \cup \{a_j\} = \{a_i, a_j\}$, while wx_iyx_iz and wx_jyx_jz represent $\{a_i\} \cup \{a_i\} = \{a_i\}$ and $\{a_j\}$, respectively. If the device behaves rationally, in the sense of (i), then it must give an output corresponding to alternative a_j when given as input any description of the set $\{a_i, a_j\}$ or of the set $\{a_j\}$. In view of (iii) this alternative must be always represented by the same output string, so the device's input-output function must satisfy

$$G(wx_iyx_jz) = G(wx_jyx_iz) = G(wx_jyx_jz).$$

Let the length of this output be L; from proposition (iv) this length can be decomposed in three ways:

$$\begin{aligned} L &= \lambda(G(wx_iyx_jz)) = f_2(x_i) + f_4(x_j) + \beta \\ &= \lambda(G(wx_jyx_iz)) = f_2(x_j) + f_4(x_i) + \beta \\ &= \lambda(G(wx_jyx_jz)) = f_2(x_j) + f_4(x_j) + \beta, \end{aligned}$$

where $\beta = f_1(w) + f_3(y) + f_5(z)$. From the first and third lines it follows that $f_2(x_i) = f_2(x_j)$, while from the second and third $f_4(x_i) = f_4(x_j)$. Clearly, the same result is obtained if x_i is the preferred alternative, by interchanging x_i and x_j throughout. This implies that

$$\begin{aligned} \lambda(G(wx_iyx_jz)) &= f_2(x_i) + f_4(x_i) + \beta \\ &= f_2(x_j) + f_4(x_j) + \beta \\ &= \lambda(G(wx_jyx_jz)) = L. \end{aligned}$$

Since this holds for all i and j, it follows that every input of the form wx_iyx_iz causes the device to give an output of the same length, namely L.

However, the output alphabet is finite, say of size n, so there can be at most n^L distinct output strings of length L. Thus for a sufficiently large number (larger than n^L) of different inputs of this form, there must be at least two such distinct inputs, say $wx_{i^*}yx_{i^*}z$ and $wx_{j^*}yx_{j^*}z$, where $i^* \neq j^*$, for which the device gives precisely the same output. This is clearly a contradiction, however, since these two inputs represent disjoint sets of alternatives, namely, $\{a_{i^*}\}$ and $\{a_{j^*}\}$, from which no common choice is possible.

References

[1] ARROW, K. J. *Social Choice and Individual Values*. 2d ed. New York: Wiley, 1963.

[2] BLACK, DUNCAN. *The Theory of Committees and Elections*. Cambridge: Cambridge University Press, 1958.

[3] CHOMSKY, NOAM. *Syntactic Structures*. The Hague: Mouton, 1957.

[4] DOWNS, ANTHONY. *An Economic Theory of Democracy*. New York: Harper, 1957.

[5] KRULEE, G. K., KRUCK, D. J., LANDI, D. M., AND MANELSKI, D. M. "Natural Language Inputs for a Problem-solving System," *Behavioral Science*, IX (1964), 281–88.

[6] RABIN, M. O., AND SCOTT, D. "Finite Automata and Their Decision Problems," *IBM Journal of Research and Development*, III (1959), 114–25.

[7] RIKER, W. H. *The Theory of Political Coalitions*. New Haven: Yale University Press, 1962.

[8]   SHEPHERDSON, J. C. "The Reduction of Two-way Automata to One-Way Automata," *IBM Journal of Research and Development*, III (1959), 198–200.

[9]   SIMON, H. A. *Models of Man*. New York: Wiley, 1957.

[10]   ——. "Theories of Decision-Making in Economics and Behavioral Science," *American Economic Review*, XLIX (1959), 253–83.

Experimental Verification of Two Theories about n-Person Games[*]

3 William H. Riker
University of Rochester

GAMES are paradigms for many kinds of political activity: bargaining, coalition formation, battles, elections, and so forth. The development over the last two decades of an elaborate mathematical theory of games therefore gives promise of a mathematical theory of politics which explains political behavior at least as well as neoclassical economic theory explains economic behavior. Despite the promise, however, political scientists have a right to be somewhat skeptical of deductions from the theory until these have been verified in some reasonably convincing ways. This essay is a modest effort at providing some verification. Unfortunately the verification which is produced from an experimental game concerns the theory of games itself rather than a political theory based on it. Still, the confidence these results give in the theory of games ought to encourage one to derive a political theory from the mathematical theory.

The minimally exacting expectations that one can have for experiments which verify theories by using human subjects are:

(1) The theories should offer a *precise* prediction of what humans are supposed to do in given circumstances. I wish to avoid the ambiguities of theories like psychoanalysis or structural-functional sociology which can always be interpreted after the fact to have predicted whatever behavior occurred. I also wish to avoid the kind of experiments on games often conducted by psychologists in which one looks at the results to utter the hypotheses.

(2) The predictions themselves should be nonobvious. In the first place, I wish to avoid the verification of trivialities such as the observation that most people prefer more money to less. The con-

* The research reported in this paper was supported by the National Science Foundation.

cern with the nonobvious is much deeper than this, however, for only with the nonobvious prediction can one be sure that the theory genuinely embodies a facet of behavior. If the prediction is obvious, the subjects in a sense consciously cooperate with the experimenter to verify the theory. But if the prediction is non-obvious, then, if the theory seems to be confirmed, one can be certain that the subjects' cooperation in confirming it was fully unconscious and unintended. And if one is thus certain, one can have substantial confidence in the theory.

(3) Finally, the coincidence between prediction and observed behavior should be sufficiently large for one to be able confidently to con-clude that the theory has been verified. If one can use the usual statistical techniques to measure coincidence, then confidence is a matter of the choice of a statistical standard. In the kind of ex-periments discussed here, however, no statistical standard is ob-viously appropriate. Hence the judgment on coincidence must be made on more or less intuitive grounds.

The theories and experiments to be discussed in this essay clearly satisfy the first two conditions. Whether or not they satisfy the third, the reader himself must judge.

In this essay two similar theories are tested. One is the von Neumann-Morgenstern definition [5] of a solution for three-person zero-sum (or constant-sum) games. The other is the Aumann-Maschler theory [1] of the bargaining set for three-person non-zero-sum (or non-constant-sum) games. These two theories provide similar normative standards for the two kinds of three-person games.

The von Neumann-Morgenstern definition of a solution for n-person games is developed as follows: There is a set of players $N: (1, 2, \ldots, n)$ whose purpose is to obtain payoffs by arranging themselves in coalitions. For each coalition, S, $S \in N$, there is a value, v, which has the following properties:

(1) $\qquad v(\Phi) = 0$, where Φ is the empty set,

(2) $\qquad v(S) = -v(-S)$, which is the zero-sum condition,

(3) $\qquad v(I) = 0$, where I is the set of all players,

(4) $\quad v(SUT) \geqq v(S) + v(T)$, where S and T are disjoint subsets of N.

For convenience it is assumed that $v(\{i\}) = -\gamma$, where $\{i\}$ is a coalition of a single player by himself and thus that $-\gamma$ is the worst payoff that a player can receive. An *imputation*, x, is a set of payoffs, $x = (x_1, x_2, \ldots, x_n)$, to all the members of N and has the following properties:

(5) $$x_i \geq v(\{i\})$$

(6) $$\sum_{i=1}^{n} x_i = 0.$$

Item (5) asserts that, no matter what coalition players arrange themselves in, the ith player will not accept a payoff less than what he can receive alone, which is $-\gamma$. Item (6) is the zero-sum condition. A set, S, is called *effective* for an imputation x if

(7) $$\sum_{i \in S} x_i \leq v(S),$$

which is to say that players "are convinced or can be convinced" that they can actually obtain x_i and that they reject as idle dreams imputations which offer more than $v(S)$. Finally, an imputation x is said to *dominate* an imputation y if there exists a set S with the following properties:

(8) S is not empty.

(9) S is effective for x.

(10) $x_i > y_i$, for all i in S.

With this vocabulary, it is now possible to define a solution. A set, V, of imputations is said to be a *solution* if it possesses the following properties:

(11)   Every y not in V is dominated by some x in V.

(12)   No y in V is dominated by an x in V.

With respect to the three-person zero-sum game, the set V is the following imputations, when $v(\{i\}) = -\gamma$:

$$V = \begin{cases} (\gamma/2, & \gamma/2, & -\gamma) \\ (\gamma/2, & -\gamma, & \gamma/2) \\ (-\gamma, & \gamma/2, & \gamma/2) \end{cases}.$$

Or, if $v(\{i\}) = -1$, as in the normalized zero-sum formulation:

$$V = \begin{cases} (\ \tfrac{1}{2}, & \tfrac{1}{2}, & -1) \\ (\ \tfrac{1}{2}, & -1, & \tfrac{1}{2}) \\ (-1, & \tfrac{1}{2}, & \tfrac{1}{2}) \end{cases}.$$

Or, if $v(\{i\}) = 0$, as in the constant-sum formulation:

$$V = \begin{cases} x: & (\tfrac{1}{2}, & \tfrac{1}{2}, & 0) \\ y: & (\tfrac{1}{2}, & 0, & \tfrac{1}{2}) \\ z: & (\ 0, & \tfrac{1}{2}, & \tfrac{1}{2}) \end{cases}.$$

If one considers the constant-sum form, it is apparent that this set of three imputations satisfies the definition of a solution. For some imputation, w, let $w_1 > \frac{1}{2}$. Then $w_2 < \frac{1}{2}$ and $w_3 < \frac{1}{2}$. Hence, with respect to the coalition S, $S: \{2, 3\}$, $z_2 > w_2$ and $z_3 > w_3$ so that z dominates w. By suitable permutations of $w_i > \frac{1}{2}$, it follows that y dominates any w in which $w_3 > \frac{1}{2}$ and x dominates any w in which $w_2 > \frac{1}{2}$. Since the imputations in V exhaust the possibilities in which two players divide equally, all imputations not in V must impute to some player an amount greater than $\frac{1}{2}$. Hence all imputations not in V are dominated by some imputation in V. On the other hand, since $x_1 = y_1$, $x_2 = z_2$, and $y_3 = z_3$, no imputation in V can satisfy (10) and hence no imputation in V can dominate another in V.

The intuitive notion behind this definition is that the set V embodies a kind of stability. Once an imputation in V is arrived at, no member of a winning coalition has any incentive to defect to another imputation in V. Furthermore, once an imputation in V is arrived at, any member of a winning coalition who defects from it runs the very great risk of ending up a loser. For example, if the imputation $x = (\frac{1}{2}, \frac{1}{2}, 0)$ is arrived at and player 2 is tempted to break away from it by $w = (0, \frac{3}{4}, \frac{1}{4})$, he should consider 1's obvious answer to w is to offer player 3 the imputation $y = (\frac{1}{2}, 0, \frac{1}{2})$ in which 2 receives nothing. In short, an obvious punishment exists in V for any player who deserts an imputation in V. In this sense, V possesses both an inner and an outer stability.

Most of our subjects phrased this stability somewhat differently, emphasizing the notion of trust. They interpreted any imputation not in V as an invitation to the player receiving $x_i < \frac{1}{2}$ as an invitation to that player to desert to some coalition which provided an imputation in V. After the players learned the game, if player 1, for example, offered to split the winnings so that he received two-fifths and player 2 received three-fifths, player 2 commonly responded with the question: "How do I know that you won't go 50–50 with player 3?" Because this question is unanswerable in any convincing way, our subjects tended to trust each other only with an imputation in V.

Whether one interprets the stability of V in terms of the difficulty of arriving at anything "better," as do von Neumann and Morgenstern, or in terms of trust (and these are, I believe, two sides of the same coin), it is apparent that there is some kind of stability in the set V. The essence of this stability seems to be the fact that a player receives the same amount from each of the winning coalitions he can be in.

This feature is captured in the Aumann-Maschler definition of a bargaining set for n-person non-zero-sum games, which is similar to but somewhat more precise than the von Neumann-Morgenstern solution for the same category. The Aumann-Maschler idea is developed thus: There is a set N: $\{1, 2, \ldots, n\}$ of players and a set $\{\beta\}$ of permissible coalitions which are nonempty subsets, B, of N. For each B, there is a number $v(B)$, which is the value of the coalition B. As in the case of zero-sum theory a minimum value is assigned to the single member coalition:

(13) $$v(\{i\}) = 0.$$

And it is assumed, for all coalitions,

(14) $$v(B) \geq 0.$$

A payoff configuration (p.c.), which is comparable to an imputation, is a statement of the following form:

(15) $$(\chi; \beta) = (x_1, x_2, \ldots, x_n; B_1, B_2, \ldots, B_m)$$

such that $B_1, B_2, \ldots, B_m$ are mutually disjoint sets of $\{B\}$ whose union is N.

A p.c., like an imputation, is a possible outcome of a play of the game; but some possible outcomes are unrealistic (e.g., where $x_i < 0$ because of (13)), so one can impose on the notion of a p.c. a condition comparable to (5) but limited to the payoffs within coalitions. Thus for each B, $B \subset B_j, j = 1, 2, \ldots, m$

(16) $$\sum_{i \epsilon B} x_i \geq v(B).$$

A configuration satisfying (16) is called a coalitionally rational payoff configuration, c.r.p.c. It is rational in the sense that, for each of the disjoint coalitions into which N is divided, the players in the coalition receive at least as much as the coalition is worth.

To define the bargaining set generally would take more space than is here available. (See Aumann and Maschler [1].) But its development for the three-person case can be stated relatively briefly: Given a coalition, (i, j), and a c.r.p.c., x, an *objection* by i against j to x is the proposal of a new c.r.p.c., y, based on a new coalition, (i, k), such that i does better in y than in x and k does at least as well. That is,

(17) $$y_i > x_i \quad \text{and} \quad y_k \geq x_k.$$

A *counterobjection* by j against i to y is the proposal of still another c.r.p.c., z, based on a coalition, (j, k), such that both j and k do at least as well in z as in their immediate alternatives, x and y. That is,

(18) $$z_j \geq x_j \quad \text{and} \quad z_k \geq y_k.$$

A c.r.p.c. is said to be *stable* if, for each objection of i against j to x, it is possible for j to offer a counterobjection. The set of all stable c.r.p.c.'s is the *bargaining set*, M. A stable c.r.p.c. is one in which each partner is doing as well as he can in the sense that any departure from it in favor of one partner will allow the other partner to find a better arrangement. Hence the set of stable c.r.p.c.'s is the set of configurations from which it is unwise to depart.

This rather complicated definition may be clarified by an example of a three-person game in which

$$(19) \quad \begin{cases} v\left(\{i\}\right) = 0 \\ v\left(1, 2\right) = 4 \\ v\left(1, 3\right) = 5 \\ v\left(2, 3\right) = 6 \\ v\left(1, 2, 3\right) = 0. \end{cases}$$

The set, M, for this game is:

$$(20) \quad \begin{cases} (0, 0, 0; 1, 2, 3) \\ (1\tfrac{1}{2}, 2\tfrac{1}{2}, 0; 12, 3) \\ (1\tfrac{1}{2}, 0, 3\tfrac{1}{2}; 13, 2) \\ (0, 2\tfrac{1}{2}, 3\tfrac{1}{2}; 23, 1). \end{cases}$$

Suppose $(x; \beta) = (1\tfrac{1}{2}, 2\tfrac{1}{2}, 0; 12, 3)$, and suppose that player 1 proposes the objection, $y = (2, 0, 3; 13, 2)$. This is a valid objection as defined by (17) for $y_1 > x_1$ and $y_3 \geq x_3$. But since 1 receives somewhat more than the set M suggests is reasonable and 3 receives less, player 2 can offer the counterobjection, $z = (0, 2\tfrac{1}{2}, 3\tfrac{1}{2}; 23, 1)$. This is a valid counterobjection as defined by (18) because $z_2 \geq x_2$ and $z_3 \geq y_3$. By a similar argument, every departure from M can be shown to be unstable in the sense that, if i initiates a departure from $(x \epsilon M; ij, k)$, then j can offer a feasible alternative in which i is left out and j and his allies do as well as or better than they did in x.

On the other hand, no c.r.p.c. not a member of (20) can be shown to be stable. Suppose $(x; \beta) = (1\tfrac{1}{2} + \epsilon, 2\tfrac{1}{2} - \epsilon, 0; 12, 3)$, where $0 < \epsilon < 2\tfrac{1}{2}$. Suppose also that player 2 offers an objection $y = (0, 2\tfrac{1}{2}, 3\tfrac{1}{2}; 23, 1)$. This satisfies the definition (17), for $y_2 > x_2$ and $y_3 \geq x_3$. But player 1 cannot offer a counterobjection, for his counter, z, must be such that $z = (1\tfrac{1}{2} + \epsilon, 0, 3\tfrac{1}{2} - \epsilon)$. This does not satisfy (18), for, while $z_1 \geq x_1$, still it is not true that $z_3 \geq y_3$. In x, player 1 is receiving more than M suggests he is "worth," so that he cannot offer a valid counterobjection to player 2's proposal to leave x.

The intuitive idea involved in singling out the set M as the bargaining set is similar to the intuitive notion of a von Neumann-Morgenstern solution to zero-sum games. It is simply that, once a payoff configuration in M is reached, it is in some sense unreasonable to depart from it. Suppose players 1 and 2 have agreed on $(1\frac{1}{2}, 2\frac{1}{2}, 0; 12, 3)$. Then 1, for example, has no motive to propose an alternative in the set [e.g. $(1\frac{1}{2}, 0, 3\frac{1}{2}; 13, 2)$] for he receives the same amount in both configurations. Furthermore, he has no motive to propose a configuration outside M. Suppose he proposes $(2, 0, 3; 13, 2)$. Then there is every expectation that $(0, 2\frac{1}{2}, 3\frac{1}{2}; 23, 1)$ will form in which player 1 is completely left out. As out subjects often expressed it, when a configuration in M is formed, one could "trust" one's partner; otherwise not.

The Experimental Design

The subjects in Experiment I were 27 male sophomore students at the University of Rochester who had applied for part-time employment at one of the several employment offices in the university. They were therefore presumably interested in obtaining as much money as possible. (Subsequent experiments with students chosen in different ways suggest, however, that the need for money is not an observably significant factor in behavior.) Subjects in Experiment II were 27 male evening students in the graduate college of business ranging in age from 25 to 55 and in occupation from management trainee and mailman to department head at the largest local industrial plant.

In both experiments three subjects played a trial of the game, the object of which was to form a coalition of two players to divide up the stakes provided by the experimenter. In Experiment I the game was constant sum with the following payoff schedule:

If $(\{1\}, \{2\}, \{3\})$ forms, players receive nothing.

If $(1, 2)$, $(1, 3)$, or $(2, 3)$ forms, the coalition receives \$3.00 to be divided among the members as decided in the course of the play.

If $(1, 2, 3)$ forms, players receive nothing.

In Experiment II the game was non-zero sum with the following payoff schedule:

If $(\{1\}, \{2\}, \{3\})$ forms, players receive nothing.

If $(1, 2)$ forms, players 1 and 2 receive \$4.00, to be divided as decided in the course of the play.

If $(1, 3)$ forms, players 1 and 3 receive \$5.00, to be divided as decided in the course of the play.

If $(2, 3)$ forms, players 2 and 3 receive \$6.00, to be divided as decided in the course of the play.

If $(1, 2, 3)$ forms, players receive nothing.

In both experiments players were asked to negotiate by pairs over the prospective division of the payoff. The negotiations were conducted according to the following schedule:

Five minutes
(or less if they had nothing more to say)
Players   1, 2   1, 3   2, 3

Three minutes
(or less if they had nothing more to say)
Players   1, 2   1, 3   2, 3

In experiment I players were guaranteed the first three conversations, and the trial was stopped at some randomly chosen time in the course of the later possible conversations. In Experiment II all six conversations were guaranteed. Negotiations between each pair were conducted in the presence of the experimenters and a tape recorder while the third player waited in another room. During the course of a play, subjects were allowed no contact with each other outside the experiment room.

At the end of negotiations players were asked privately and individually if they had formed a coalition; if so, with whom and at what division of the stakes. If two persons agreed on their answers to these three questions, they were paid by the experimenter; otherwise not.

Care was taken that subjects in each trial did not know each other before engaging in the play. Since the experiments were conducted over nine-week and six-week periods, however, subjects learned who other subjects were and discussed the game, strategies for playing it, the behavior of other players, and so forth. Especially during Experiment I (with undergraduates in residence), the game became a subject of campus gossip. Since this was not an experiment in learning but rather one to determine behavior among relatively sophisticated subjects, this discussion was welcomed by the experimenters.

The predictions were, of course, that in Experiment I players would choose one of the following imputations:

if $(1, 2)$ formed, $(1.50, 1.50, 0)$,
if $(1, 3)$ formed, $(1.50, 0, 1.50)$,
if $(2, 3)$ formed, $(0, 1.50, 1.50)$,

which together form the set, V, for the given game; and that in Experiment II players would choose one of the following payoff configurations, which together form all but $(0, 0, 0)$ of the set, M, for the given game:

> if (1, 2) formed, (1.50, 2.50, 0),
> if (1, 3) formed, (1.50, 0, 3.50),
> if (2, 3) formed, (0, 2.50, 3.50),

It should be noted, of course, that V and M do not involve predictions about which particular coalitions will form. Rather they simply involve a prediction about how any coalition that does form will divide the stakes internally.

The Results

As is apparent from Table 3.1, out of 26 trials, 19 (or about three-fourths) in Experiment I came out exactly as predicted. Of the seven which did not, three involved deliberate "irrationalities" on the part of one subject in each set. On trials 10 and 16 a subject, who was opposed to the moral principles which he (mistakenly) believed animated the experiments, consciously tried to behave in an irrational way. On trial 10 he adamantly demanded $2.00, fully expecting to lose, but nevertheless won because the other two subjects failed to agree. On trial 16 he proposed that the three divide the money equally (thus turning the subjects into a three-person coalition against the experimenter in a four-person game). Since the announced payoff prohibited such an arrangement, he proposed $1.00 for himself and $2.00 for his partner, trusting his partner to give $1.00 to the loser later (which, I understand, was done). On trial 21 player 3 was intensely angered by player 1, with whom he thought he had a firm agreement at the end of their first conversation. When he subsequently discovered he did not, he went to unnecessarily extreme lengths to break up the agreement between players 1 and 2, which resulted in a payment to himself of $1.15.

While these three deviations clearly represent accidents or "noise" in the system, the other four represent a conscious rejection of the principle involved in the notion of V. In these cases, one of the subjects believed that it was better to win less in order to be certain of winning. In the language of Siegel and Fouraker, these players had a lower level of aspiration. In Fouraker's experiments [2] with a non-constant-sum game, the level of aspiration turned out to be an important determinant of behavior, with those having a low level winning consistently. In these experiments with a zero-sum game, however, a low level of aspiration turned out to be self-defeating. As one subject remarked, "At first I thought the best way to play was to take a little less to be sure of getting a partner, but after the first game I found that nobody trusts you if you ask for less than $1.50." It is notable that three of the four instances of

Table 3.1. Results of Experiment I

	Outcomes		
	Players		
Trials	1	2	3
1	0	1.65	1.35
2	1.55	0	1.45
3	1.50	1.50	0
4	1.50	1.50	0
5	1.50	1.50	0
6	1.35	1.65	0
7	1.50	0	1.50
8	0	1.50	1.50
9	1.50	1.50	0
Averages 1–9 *	1.4867	1.5428	1.45
10	2.00	0	1.00
11	1.50	0	1.50
12	0	1.50	1.50
13	1.50	1.50	0
14	1.50	1.50	0
15	1.50	1.50	0
16	1.00	0	2.00
17	1.50	1.50	0
18	1.50	1.50	0
19	0	1.60	1.40
20	0	1.50	1.50
21	0	1.85	1.15
22	0	1.50	1.50
23	1.50	0	1.50
24	0	1.50	1.50
25	1.50	1.50	0
26	1.50	1.50	0
Averages 1–26 *	1.50	1.54	1.45

	Divisions			
Trials	1.50 to 1.50	1.51–1.60 to 1.49–1.40	1.61–2.00 to 1.39–1.00	Totals
1–9	6	1	2	9
10–26	13	1	3	17
All	19	2	5	26

* These are averages of the winners only.

outcomes based on one subject's low level of aspiration occurred in the first nine games which were orientation games for the 27 subjects.

In the beginning of this paper, I set forth three standards that experiments using human subjects ought to meet. They seem to be met in this instance. The prediction is quite precise for it states exactly the division to be expected. The prediction is to some slight degree nonobvious, as indicated by the fact that at least some subjects did not originally see the importance of the set V. Finally, the prediction seems to be reasonably well verified inasmuch as the subjects performed as predicted about three-fourths of the time. But the verification is stronger even than this fact indicates. Since the alternative to V, that is, a low level of aspiration, which showed up one-third of the time in the first round of trials, almost entirely disappeared from the two subsequent rounds of trials, it may be concluded that sophisticated subjects (i.e., second-, third-, and, in a few cases, fourth-time players) rejected the alternative theory and chose to use the standard of V. Altogether this experiment seems to provide a very high degree of verification of the von Neumann-Morgenstern solution of n-person zero-sum games.

When one turns to the second experiment, however, the degree of verification declines. The prediction is, of course, equally precise. And it is certainly nonobvious. While it may appear obvious to some readers when presented in the form of the bargaining set, i.e.,[1]

$$\mathrm{M} = \begin{cases} (1\frac{1}{2},\ 2\frac{1}{2},\ 0) \\ (1\frac{1}{2},\ 0,\ 3\frac{1}{2}) \\ (0,\ 2\frac{1}{2},\ 3\frac{1}{2}) \end{cases}$$

still it is far less obvious when presented in the characteristic function form, i.e.,

if (1, 2) forms, it receives \$4.00,
if (1, 3) forms, it receives \$5.00,
if (2, 3) forms, it receives \$6.00.

Since it was presented to our subjects in the latter form, it is perhaps not surprising that *not a single one of them recognized the existence of the bargaining set*, even after playing from three to seven times. It is difficult for a prediction to be more nonobvious than that.[2]

---

[1] The bargaining set also contains the outcome (0, 0, 0), but we exclude it from consideration here. It appears in the set only because it technically satisfies the definition. And although it occurs in our experiments by accident, no one ever consciously sought to bring it about.

[2] In a more recent and as yet unanalyzed experiment with this game in which undergraduate subjects were used, we were surprised that in their first play several subjects told us about the bargaining set. When we inquired how they reached the conclusion

Given the fact that none of the subjects observed the bargaining set, the outcomes of Experiment II, which are set forth in Table 3.2, seem to provide some verification of the prediction. Seven of the thirty-three, or about one-fifth, came out exactly as predicted, while four more, bringing the proportion to one-third, came out very close to what was predicted. Furthermore, since the groups of subjects often scorned to bargain by nickels and dimes and only regarded offers of quarters as significant, it is probably reasonable to regard all deviations up to twenty-five cents as "close" to the bargaining set. If so, about three-fifths of the trials may be regarded as verifications of the predictions. The main alternative to the notion of the bargaining set (at least in these trials) is the principle of even division, which also was applied seven times. But in all trials other than these seven, the subjects consciously rejected the principle of even division while seeming to work toward something close to the bargaining set. That the subjects rejected equal division is clearly seen when one looks at the averages, as in Table 3.3. If the equal division principle had been applied by the subjects, they would have come out with the averages in the last row of this table, which is, for this experiment, a very bad prediction for columns one and three. But the first row of the table, the bargaining set prediction, is quite close to the actual outcomes for all three players. Hence the experiment provides some verification of the prediction in terms of the averages. It appears that (except for the seven possible instances of a conscious adoption of a different principle) the subjects either arrived at a payoff configuration in the bargaining set or varied randomly around these configurations, presumably according to the unique personality and bargaining factors present in each trial.

The reasons subjects most often gave for arriving at something close to the bargaining set equilibrium are fully consonant with the theory. They emphasized in discussions that, if one person received "too large" offers from each of the others, then it would be advantageous for the other two to combine against him. So there was a tendency to shy away from divisions very far from the predictions of the bargaining set. It was not that players calculated from the bargaining set, but they did calculate from the history of offers given to them what the possible consequences of these offers would be. And these practical calculations are what drove them to the bargaining set.

Two other experiments have been conducted with similar three-person games. Maschler [4] has conducted experiments with many non-

---

that it was "the solution," each replied, "I solved the simultaneous equations." The businessmen subjects of Experiment II, mostly men some distance in time from undergraduate algebra courses, could hardly be expected to analyze the game in this way—and they did not.

Table 3.2. Results of Experiment II

	Outcomes		
	Players		
Trials	**1**	**2**	**3**
1	0	2.00	4.00
2	0	2.75	3.25
3	0	2.25	3.75
4	1.50	0	3.50
5	2.00	2.00	0
6	0	2.20	3.80
7	1.00	0	4.00
8	0	2.40	3.60
9	1.75	2.25	0
10	1.50	0	3.50
11	2.00	0	3.00
12	2.00	2.00	0
13	1.25	0	3.75
14	0	3.00	3.00
15	0	2.75	3.25
16	1.00	3.00	0
17	0	3.00	3.00
18	1.00	0	4.00
19	0	3.00	3.00
20	1.50	2.50	0
21	1.25	0	3.75
22	1.75	0	3.25
23	1.50	2.50	0
24	0	2.00	4.00
25	2.00	2.00	0
26	0	2.50	3.50
27	0	2.40	3.60
28	2.00	2.00	0
29	1.45	0	3.55
30	0	0	0
31	1.50	2.50	0
32	1.50	0	3.50
33	0	2.40	3.60
Averages *	1.55	2.42	3.53

Divisions	
As predicted	7
Deviations	
Up to ±.10	4
From ±.11 to ±.25	7
From ±.26 to ±.50	14
No coalition	1
Total	33

* These are averages of the winners only.

constant-sum games (one trial per game) using Israeli secondary school students. In general his experiments tend to verify the predictions of the bargaining set in about the same manner as the experiment reported here does. Lieberman [3] has conducted experiments with one non-constant-sum game, using Harvard undergraduates, with the following bargaining set:

$$M = \begin{cases} Player & 1 & 2 & 3 \\ & 6, & 4, & -10 \\ & 6, & -8, & 2 \\ & -6, & 4, & 2 \end{cases}.$$

In Lieberman's experiments much the most frequent outcome (182 out of 320 instances) is an equal division. The differences among these experi-

Table 3.3. Average outcomes for Experiment II, actual and predicted under the principles of equal division and the bargaining set

Average when winner	Players		
	1	2	3
Bargaining set (predicted)	1.50	2.50	3.50
Actual	1.55	2.42	3.53
Equal division (predicted) *	2.26	2.59	2.78

* Given the coalitions which actually occurred.

mental outcomes may be largely accounted for by institutional factors built into the experimental design. Maschler's subjects bargained face-to-face and lengthily. As might be expected, therefore, his subjects came close to the bargaining set, just as mine did. Lieberman's subjects, on the other hand, communicated by turning cards and for only a few moments. Since they were rushed for time, they chose what is probably the easiest method of generating trust quickly, namely, equal division. In short, Maschler's institutions and mine created a bias toward the bargaining set, Lieberman's a bias toward equal division. Given the fact that institutional factors have a great influence over outcomes and that Maschler's and my conditions embodied the assumptions of the theory (i.e., a considerable amount of time to bargain) while Lieberman's did not, the results seem to be persuasive evidence for the validity of the bargaining set prediction.

Nevertheless, the bargaining set prediction for non-zero-sum games cannot, by these experiments, be regarded as nearly as well verified as the solution prediction for zero-sum games. Inasmuch as non-zero-sum games are vastly more complicated than zero-sum games, this result is not at all surprising. What is surprising, I believe, is that the bargaining set prediction is as well verified as it is.

Assuming that both experiments provide at least some verification for the theories in question, assuming indeed that these game theoretic ideas are not only normative but also descriptive, then the conclusion follows that subjects in experiments with games behave "rationally" if "rationality" is defined as a preference for the standards of behavior involved in the notions of V and M. Turning from experiments with games to politics, we can infer two things about the political world. One is that participants in it also behave or try to behave rationally. The other is that there are standards of rational behavior that, in theory at least, can be discerned. Hence, if one discerns them, one can predict political behavior.

References

[1] AUMANN, ROBERT J., AND MASCHLER, MICHAEL. "The Bargaining Set for Cooperative Games," in M. Dresher, L. S. Shapley, and A. W. Tucker, eds., *Advances in Game Theory*. (Annals of Mathematical Studies, No. 52.) Princeton, N.J.: Princeton University Press, 1964.

[2] FOURAKER, L. E. "Levels of Aspiration and Group Decision-Making," in S. Messack and A. H. Brayfield, eds., *Decisions and Choice*. New York: McGraw-Hill, 1964.

[3] LIEBERMAN, BERNHART. "Experimental Studies of Conflict in Some Two and Three Person Games," in J. H. Criswell *et al.*, eds., *Mathematical Methods in Small Group Processes*. Stanford, Calif.: Stanford University Press, 1962.

[4] MASCHLER, MICHAEL. *Playing an* n-*Person Game: An Experiment*. (Princeton University Econometric Research Program, Research Memorandum No. 73.) Princeton, N.J., 1965.

[5] VON NEUMANN, JOHN, AND MORGENSTERN, OSKAR. *The Theory of Games and Economic Behavior*. 2d ed. Princeton, N.J.: Princeton University Press, 1947.

Mathematical Models for Predicting Judicial Behavior

4 S. Sidney Ulmer
University of Kentucky

Introduction

In betting on horses, we engage in a process of distinguishing prospective winners from prospective losers. The bet is merely evidence of confidence in our final choice. In choosing business executives, directors of corporations pursue a similar path, the choice having the effect of betting corporate assets on the abilities of the manager to perform satisfactorily. Obviously men are not horses. But in both cases the postulate underlying the selection process is the same, i.e., that animals (equine or human) behave consistently in terms of some set of quantitative or qualitative variables. In the case of horses there is wide agreement on such key factors as breeding, speed, jockey, and track condition as predictors of racing success. Although we have less agreement about the determinants of man's behavior, most of us would subscribe to the notion that indicators to behavioral outputs are discoverable. At least that is the belief responsible for attempts to predict human behavior in the political world. And it is responsible for the recent effort devoted to models for predicting the behavior of judges.

In his volume on *Judicial Behavior* Glendon Schubert refers to three philosophical models for predicting judicial decisions: the legal norm, the legal fact, and the legal discretion models.[1] In general, the legal norm model assumes that "facts are facts" and that judges are unlikely to disagree fundamentally as to the facts in a given situation.[2] There may be disagreement about the legally relevant facts, but if so it is a function of improper choice of legal norm. Procedural norms serve the function of initially narrowing the facts, but those finally chosen as relevant will depend on the criteria which the court decides should prevail. This

[1] *Judicial Behavior: A Reader in Theory and Research* (Chicago: Rand McNally, 1964), pp. 443 ff.

[2] In my teaching I have referred to this as the Sergeant Friday approach.

model, therefore, maximizes norm certainty and minimizes fact uncertainty. Such maximization constitutes the prediction problem.

The legal fact model suggests that facts are not as easily determined as the legal norm model implies. When judges disagree, it is not over norms but over the facts made relevant by the chosen decision rules. Thus this model emphasizes that judges are likely to disagree about what has happened before a case reaches the court and to attribute disagreement concerning outcome to differential perception. Clearly, the legal fact model minimizes disagreement about norms and defines the prediction problem as maximization of fact recognition.

The suggestion that neither legal fact nor legal norm models are adequate is a feature of the legal discretion model. This approach assumes that the discretion left to the judge makes the prediction of decisions on the basis of legal facts and norms unreliable. Consequently, emphasis is on minimizing such considerations as guides to action. This view is attributed to Hans Kelsen and his Pure Theory of Law, but Kelsen, while implying the operation of other variables, did not investigate their nature or their impact.

Schubert also refers to a modified legal discretion model which appears to take up where Kelsen leaves off—that is, it emphasizes the discretion of the judge but assumes its exercise in some patterned fashion. If these individual patterns are sufficiently understood, then reliable prediction of individual votes is thought possible.

Whereas the legal norm and legal fact models are predictive schema, the legal discretion model asserts the impossibility of prediction or at least suggests that the problem is multidimensional and perhaps incapable of solution since the wellsprings of discretion are so exceedingly complex. Or to put it another way, this model emphasizes why we cannot predict rather than suggesting how we might go about a difficult task. Consequently, I think the legal discretion model one genus, the legal norm and fact models another.

The modified legal discretion model is of still a third variety, for it, in effect, is many models or theories each emphasizing some particular factor or set of factors impinging upon decisional outcome. This is not merely a matter of approaching the subject from the perspectives of cultural anthropology, political sociology, and social psychology or of approaching the prediction problem from different levels of analysis. The latter view, which Schubert asserts, reflects his adoption of attitude as the key ingredient or category in terms of which all other facets of explanation can be treated. Indeed, he says:

One can understand and explain—at least, at a first level of initial comprehension—everything about judicial decision-making on the basis of attitudinal similarities and differences of the individuals in the decision-making group. Of course, this requires a very comprehensive analysis of individual attitudes, including both attitudes toward the issues of public policy that individuals are asked to resolve and their attitudes toward each other, and toward all other participants in the decision-making process.[3]

Now if by attitude we mean a consistent set of opinions regarding a given item or set of items, and we can assume that all individuals have such "opinion sets," then for any given decision an outcome consistent with at least one such "opinion set" seems likely. But John Sprague has suggested that "any found relationship may be characterized as an attitude under some construction of the facts."[4] He illustrates this point with the case of a judge who votes in some way out of loyalty to the executive who appointed him.

Professor Sprague's comment does not suggest any refutation of the statement attributed to Schubert unless the latter's remark is limited to the "issue in the case." For a judge may have an attitude toward the relationship of an officeholder to one who appointed him. In correspondence with the author Professor Schubert has explicitly included Presidents as "participants in the decision-making process" to which he refers above. But he has also written, "From the point of view of predicting judicial decision-making, the attitudinal approach takes the position that, given complete knowledge of the attitudes of a set of judges toward the issue or issues that they purport to resolve in a case, the analyst predicts the behavior of the judges on the basis of the imputed differentials in their attitudes."[5]

This seeming contradiction can be rationalized by defining "complete knowledge" to include information bearing on the degree to which the attitude of the judge toward the President who appointed him is an aspect of the judge's perception of the issue. But to follow this route is seriously to impair the use of "attitude" as a fruitful concept in the analysis of judicial behavior. For, to return to Sprague's point, if it means everything, then it means nothing. Rather than viewing the

---

[3] Schubert, *op. cit.*, p. 445.

[4] "Voting Patterns on the United States Supreme Court: Cases in Federalism, 1889–1959," (unpublished Ph.D. dissertation, Stanford University, 1964), p. 4. Although I think that Sprague puts his finger on the problem, I would approach it in a slightly different fashion. The relevant questions, as I see them, are: (a) Does a given judge have any consistent set of opinions toward an item or item set? (b) If so, what is the identification of the items or item sets? (c) If identified, which of the opinion sets are relevant for a given decision? (d) If more than one opinion set is consistent with the outcome, what is the relative degree to which each impinges on decision?

[5] Schubert, *op. cit.*, p. 446.

modified legal discretion model as a single attitudinal model with multiple levels, it may advance knowledge further if we perceive it as a set of discretion models—some attitudinally based and some not.

Quantitative models for predicting judicial behavior can be classified in terms of what is to be predicted, the variables to be used, and the methods by which interrelationships are to be evaluated. Table 4.1 gives

Table 4.1. Classification scheme for quantitative
models predicting judicial behavior

I. Dependent variables
   A. Decision of court
      (1) On merits of case
      (2) Other
   B. Decision of individual judge
      (1) On merits of case
      (2) Other
II. Independent variables
   A. Attributes
   B. Opinions—attitudes
   C. Contextual—environmental stimuli
III. Analytical models
   A. Psychometric
   B. Primitive—quantitative (PQ)
   C. Boolean
   D. Regression
      (1) Normal
      (2) Discriminant

a more detailed breakdown of this classificatory scheme. Obviously, the categories of this instrument could be given greater depth. We have extended them sufficiently to pick up the major quantitative models so far developed. Applying this scheme to the work of Kort, Tanenhaus, Grunbaum-Newhouse, Nagel, Schubert, and Ulmer, we can identify five model types: $I_A II_C III_B$ (Class 1); $I_A II_C III_C$ (Class 2); $I_A II_C III_D$ (Class 3); $I_{AB} II_C III_D$ (Class 4); and $I_{AB} II_B III_A$ (Class 5).

Primitive Predictive Models

Class 1 models are basically exploratory but also early quantitative approaches to the prediction problem. Such models have been used by Kort, Nagel, and the present writer. Each focused on the decisions of the Supreme Court on the merits in formal cases. Each identified contextual-environmental stimuli as the independent variables. Each used a relatively primitive form of quantitative analysis.

In 1962 the writer attempted to explain the factors leading the Supreme Court to rule for or against Negro petitioners in jury exclusion cases.[6] Negro defendants are not entitled, under the Constitution, to have one or more Negroes on every jury by which they are tried. But in interpreting the fair trial implications of the Fourteenth Amendment, the Supreme Court has consistently held that Negroes are entitled to a jury system from which they are not intentionally and systematically excluded solely on account of race and color. The reading of the relevant cases suggested that a determination of the matter depended upon the factual situation. The language used by several of the judges indicated that the exclusion of Negroes from state juries as a matter of chance was in no way illegal or unconstitutional. The problem seemed to be to discover how the Supreme Court separated chance exclusion from that which could be described as intentional and systematic racial discrimination.

There were sufficient hints in the opinions of the judges for one to consider the possibility that the Court was comparing two populations. The first was the total qualifying population from which juries or jury lists were drawn; the second was the grand or petit jury from which exclusion had been charged. But the relevant consideration for each of these populations was thought to be the ratio of whites to Negroes in each case. This ratio was expressed by an index of racial heterogeneity. The index figures for each population were then compared to see whether a difference of the observed magnitude would be expected by chance more than five times in 100. With this approach the outcome could be explained in all cases save one in the period 1935–60.

A more ambitious attempt at predicting Supreme Court decisions mathematically was undertaken by Fred Kort in 1957.[7] Kort attempted to show that in certain areas of constitutional law it was possible to identify the factual elements influencing decision, derive numerical weights for these elements in a given set of cases, and predict correctly decisions in later cases of the same type. The model he designed for this purpose ignored the reasoning of the judges and the changing composition of the Supreme Court even though twenty-five justices sat in the period analyzed. Nevertheless, using right-to-counsel cases in the period

[6] "Supreme Court Behavior in Racial Exclusion Cases: 1935–1960," *American Political Science Review*, LVI (1962), 325–30.

[7] "Predicting Supreme Court Decisions Mathematically: A Quantitative Analysis of the Right to Counsel Cases," *American Political Science Review*, LI (1957), 1–12. Kort was not the first to suggest that the vote of a group member on a given proposal can be conceptualized as a linear summation of multiple-weighted factors which have salience for him. (Cf. L. L. Thurstone, "The Isolation of Blocs in a Legislative Body by the Voting Records of Its Members," *Journal of Social Psychology*, XXXIV (1932), 425–31.) But Kort's applications to judicial data have been creative and original.

1932–47 for deriving factors and weights, Kort was able to predict, without error, all decisions in such cases in the period 1947–56.

Professor Schubert has commented at some length on Kort's assumption that facts determine decision. According to Schubert, this is a kind of mechanical jurisprudence in which controlling facts replace controlling rules. Schubert defines facts as "assertions about the observation of events that someone has perceived to have occurred in the real world." [8] Having heard such assertions from lawyers and litigants, Supreme Court Justices must then draw their inferences. It is Schubert's belief, however, that the "judge's inference will be a function, inescapably, of his own attitude toward the value he selects as the criterion for perception of the fact." [9] This leads him to the conclusion that judges dominate and control facts, not vice versa. Few would deny, of course, that attitudes and perceptions are key variables in interpreting reality. But Kort's focus is not on that question. Essentially, his inquiry has to do with the consistency of the relationships between fact and case outcome. Whether a set of decisions can be separated in terms of a set of variables chosen by an analyst is an empirical question. Kort clearly shows that such a separation is possible with his right-to-counsel data.

Franklin M. Fisher had discussed Kort's initial predictive effort in more formal terms. [10] Having identified n factors to be responsible for decisional outcome, we can define a variable X_1 which takes the value 1 or 0 depending on the presence or absence of a given factor in a given case. Since such a variable must be defined for each factor, the number of variables $(X_1, X_2, X_3 \ldots X_n)$ equals the number of factors. The prediction problem, then, is to find a set of numbers (preferably positive) $A_1, A_2, A_3 \ldots A_n$ such that the expression

$$A_1 X_1 + A_2 X_2 + A_3 X_3 \ldots A_n X_n$$

gives a higher value for cases decided for defendants than for cases decided to the contrary. This is basically a problem of finding a hyperplane

---

[8] Schubert, *op. cit.*, p. 451.

[9] *Ibid.* It is possible to overestimate the extent to which the process of drawing inferences is subjective. If a fact is nothing more than an assertion about a perception and inference is a function of attitude, then science would seem impossible. A better statement might be that judges have attitudes which influence their choice of an inference theory. This, of course, is an empirical question. Moreover, such considerations tend to become irrelevant if a fundamental similarity of such attitudes can be assumed. The fact that we can have such similarity in certain areas of life suggests that we are sometimes dealing with reality rather than with personality. In any event, scale, factor, and other attitudinal models for analyzing Supreme Court behavior assume consensual cognition of the questions posed by the cases being decided.

[10] "The Mathematical Analysis of Supreme Court Decisions: The Use and Abuse of Quantitative Methods," *American Political Science Review*, LII (1958), 321–28.

which cuts a geometrical space in such a way that all *pro* points fall on one side of the plane and all *con* points on the other.

Figure 4.1 shows a plane cutting a two-dimensional space. This diagram suggests that a weight of six or more on either factor will give a *pro* decision regardless of the weight of the second factor. The converse, obviously, is not true. A weight of less than six on either factor will not necessarily give a *con* decision. Given such a weight on one factor, the case outcome will be determined by the weight on the other factor with which it is to be combined. The diagram does suggest, however, that a weight of less than three on both factors will produce a *con* result. In sum, then, the condition under which the plane provides a perfect division is what Fisher calls condition 1; i.e., should we observe a *pro* case with a certain number of the factors present, then we must never observe a *con* case with the same factors present. This, of course, assumes perfect consistency. Since the model assumes positive and monopolar weights, once the relative weight of a factor to other factors is determined, a given level on the numerical index assures a *pro* decision.

Kort's initial predictive effort provided relative factor weights which separated his *pro* and *con* cases perfectly. However, many different hyperplanes might have performed such a function with equal success. This can be seen quite clearly in Figure 4.1. Although the plane drawn there cuts each axis at the value of 6, the *pro* and *con* cases used in this example could be separated equally well if the intersecting values were 5 and 5, 5 and 6, 6 and 8, 6 and 7, and so forth. In short, the slopes of the lines and by definition the number of hyperplanes are infinite in number. This suggests that a particular weighting scheme may provide prediction but tell little about the true importance of the various factors. Fisher's analysis also implies that a successful predictive device does not assure us that the factors used were perceived by the judges or that high-weight factors were more important than those of low weight. Consequently, the addition and subtraction of factors may have no effect on one's ability to predict case outcomes.

While one should be aware of such restrictions, they may not be particularly damaging. They deal with perception and are important considerations if that is the focus of analysis. However, the search for a theory that will explain a given set of observations is a perfectly legitimate exercise. One who develops such a theory is under no obligation to incorporate into his explanatory device matters that do not improve explanation for him. In the event of competing explanations for observed events, values of a type other than those reflected in Fisher's comments are likely to be determinative.

To his rather impressive analytical tour de force, Fisher has added some comments concerning the use of quantitative predictors in analyzing Supreme Court behavior. Essentially, his main point is that in those areas in which such predictors can be successful, they are not needed. For, he says, if we can construct a perfectly predicting weighting scheme, the cases involved are covered by clear precedents. This com-

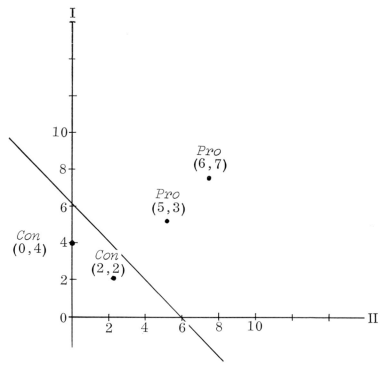

Figure 4.1. Representation of a plane cutting a two-dimensional space

ment suggests a gross misunderstanding of the judicial process. A perfectly predicting weighting scheme, at the least, identifies factors in terms of which prediction is to be made. The discovery of "clear precedent" is not always so easy. And legal analysis will not tell us whether our "clear precedent" is perceived and responded to by a given judge any more than quantitative analysis will provide that information for weighted factors in a predictive model. Moreover, Fisher fails to recognize the value of nonperfectly predicting weighting schemes. The question, always, is whether a given theory will explain a given set of facts.

We are generally interested in the extent to which such is the case, and an inadequate match is likely to lead to attempted improvement.

In spite of his generally pessimistic conclusion, however, Fisher's analysis is important for clarifying some of the problems associated with this kind of work and for suggesting the discriminant equation as a means of determining the "best" method for separating two specified classes, given that a solution exists.

The third Class 1 model features the correlation approach developed by Stuart Nagel.[11] This method follows the lead suggested by Kort in that facts or circumstances are taken as the independent variables for determining decisional outcome. Nagel, however, does not limit his model to areas of law in which decision is determined by combinations of circumstances or to single collegial courts. He notes specifically that the correlation model can handle variables relating to legal requirements, place, personnel, evidentiary facts, and the like, and that it is applicable to a set of cases decided by single- or multiple-member courts, by the same court, or by different courts. Neither does he consider the relative weight of his variables. The method assumes, in essence, that each variable is independent of each other. This may be contrasted with Kort's assumption that all factors are interdependent.

The correlation model makes use of a coefficient expressing the association of each variable with victory for the prosecution or for the defense. After the weight of each factor is determined in this fashion, a particular case is represented by the sum of the factors that appear in the case. In 1964 this method was applied to nine reapportionment cases using four facts. The cases were drawn from the Supreme Court, state courts, and lower federal courts and represented attacks on the prevailing apportionment of legislative seats in the relevant states. The result of the analysis was a perfect separation of five cases decided for the attacker and four decided against the attacker.

Each of the three Class 1 models suffers in some respect if we accept the prediction problem as defined by Fisher. Ulmer's primitive model is not appropriate for the relative weighting of variables which in combination determine decisional outcome. Nagel's correlation method assumes the independence of the operating variables, and Kort's primitive model does not provide the "best" systematic method for placing the hyperplane in the geometric space. Later analytical schemes have remedied each of these shortcomings.

[11] Stuart Nagel, "Applying Correlation Analysis to Case Prediction," *Texas Law Review*, XLII (1964), 1006–17. Cf. Stuart Nagel, "Using Simple Calculations to Predict Judicial Decisions," *Practical Lawyer*, VII (1961), 68–74, and "Statistical Prediction of Verdicts and Awards," *M.U.L.L.* (September, 1963), 135–39.

A Boolean Model

In Class 2 we may consider Kort's Boolean model.[12] Roscoe Pound has
written of the demand for a justice whose operation may be predicted in
advance of action. This implies logical relations between decisions and
antecedent considerations. Holmes, however, suggested that logic has
not been the life of law, leading Lawlor to ask: What is law without it? [13]
I would add that the implication of Pound's statement is closer to reality
than is that of Holmes's suggestion. Of course, the Justice spoke for
emphasis and not for literal meaning. But the logical relationships between decision and antecedent cause might have been there all the time—
unnoted. This would be to commit the error of false identification of
antecedents—the identification of the "ought cause" rather than the
"real cause."

The distinctive characteristic of the Boolean model is its concern *only*
with logical relations; it does not assign numerical weights. As in Kort's
primitive model, facts are used as independent variables. But no assumption as to the linearity (additive quality) of the facts is necessary. And
the model avoids the postulate that the scoring system used for the variables is the "best" for placing cases on a numerical index. Otherwise, the
Boolean model makes an inquiry similar to that of Kort's first model.
Thus Kort recommends it when one is interested in predicting outcome in
a case involving a combination of facts that has not appeared although
using facts that have appeared in other combinations.

Since the facts used in the model are monopolar, a *pro* decision may be
anticipated in any case having a set of facts which includes the smallest
combination giving a *pro* decision. Or, to put it another way,

$$R(C_1) \geq R(C_2) \to D_{pro} \leftrightarrow R(C_2) \to D_{pro}.$$

This says that the rank of a case that is equal to or higher than the rank
of a second case implies a decision for defendant if and only if the rank of
the second case implies a *pro* decision. For example, consider five cases
with four facts distributed as follows:

Cases	Facts	Rank	Decision
C_1	$f_1 f_2 f_3 f_4$	1	*Pro*
C_2	$f_1 f_2 f_3$	2	*Pro*
C_3	$f_1 f_2$	3	*Pro*
C_4	$f_1\ f_3$		*Con*
C_5	$f_2\ f_4$		*Con*

[12] Fred Kort, "Simultaneous Equations and Boolean Algebra in the Analysis of
Judicial Decisions," in Hans Baade (ed.), *Jurimetrics* (New York: Basic Books, 1963),
pp. 143–63.

[13] Reed C. Lawlor, "What Computers Can Do: Analysis and Prediction of Judicial
Decisions," *American Bar Association Journal*, XLIX (1963), 339.

If a case characterized by a set of facts and a *pro* decision is compared to a case containing the same facts plus at least one more, the latter is said to have a higher rank than the former. Ranking our *pro* cases, we get the order C_1, C_2, C_3. Applying the foregoing statement, we assert that if the rank of C_1 is equal to or higher than the rank of C_2, then a *pro* decision is expected if and only if the rank of C_2 gives a *pro* decision. Since C_1 is ranked first, C_2 second, and C_2 is *pro*, C_1 must be decided in the same direction to maintain consistency. The prediction equations can be written

$$D_{pro} \leftrightarrow f_1 \wedge f_2$$
$$D_{con} \leftrightarrow \sim(f_1 \vee f_2).$$

Obviously, the application of this method to large numbers of variables necessitates the use of computer facilities. But the complexity of large numbers does not appreciably affect the simplicity of the prediction equation, although it motivates the use of set and subset notation. Thus an analysis of 100 variables would probably be prohibitive without machine help. The prediction equation, on the other hand, could be written simply as:

$$D_{pro} \leftrightarrow f_1 \wedge (f_3 \vee f_4) \vee (\text{L3}, \text{Sa}) \vee (\text{L8}, \text{Sb}) \wedge (\text{L12}, \text{Sc})$$

where

$$Sa = f_5 - f_{15}; \; Sb = f_{16} - f_{75}; \; Sc = f_{76} - f_{100}.$$

We have remarked that the Boolean model does not derive numerical weights for the operating factors. But a weighting is achieved, though in a different sense, for a higher-ranked case may be conceptualized as having a sum of weights that exceeds that of lower-ranked cases. What we do not know is the contribution that each factor makes toward correct prediction. Figure 4.2 is a diagram representing the possible combinations of two facts in a geometrical space. Unity indicates the presence of a fact, zero its absence. The four possibilities are:

$$f_1(1, 0); \quad f_2(0, 1); \quad f_1 \wedge f_2(1, 1); \quad \text{and} \quad \sim f_1 \wedge f_2(0, 0).$$

The rank of the *pro* cases would be C_1, C_2. Since C_1 is *pro*, C_2 must be decided the same way. Similarly, since C_3 is a *con* case, C_4 must be characterized in the same fashion. This tells us that the plane must cut to the left of C_1 and to the right of C_3. But clearly the Boolean model gives no guidance as to a more precise location or slope of the line. Thus it may be compared to Kort's primitive model which determined the slope systematically but used a formula developed by experimentation. Although that attempt has received legitimate criticism, it recognized the problem and the need for a solution in contrast to the Boolean model, which ignores these matters.

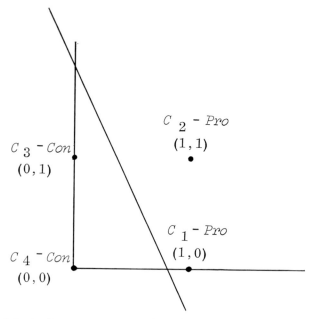

Figure 4.2. A diagram representing the possible combinations of two facts in a geometrical space. A 1 indicates the presence and 0 the absence of a fact.

Regression Models

Class 3 and 4 models address themselves specifically to the problem described above by utilizing some form of regression analysis. Normal regression models have been used by Tanenhaus *et al.*, Kort, and Grunbaum-Newhouse. Tanenhaus and his students have investigated the process by which the Supreme Court accepts or rejects certiorari applications.[14] They began by assuming that Supreme Court Rule 19 does not provide a satisfactory explanation for the Court's exercise of its certiorari jurisdiction; that the pressure on the Justices' time is such that only cursory attention can be given to most certiorari applications; and that a substantial percentage of certiorari applications are so frivolous as to merit no attention at all. Given the validity of these postulates, their hypothesis—that a group of cues exists which warns a Justice when a case needs serious study—is eminently reasonable.

[14] Joseph Tanenhaus, Marvin Schick, Matthew Muraskin, and Daniel Rosen, "The Supreme Court's Certiorari Jurisdiction: Cue Theory," in Glendon Schubert (ed.), *Judicial Decision Making* (New York: Free Press of Glencoe, 1963), pp. 111–32.

Unlike the models discussed earlier, the cue regression model makes no attempt to predict outcome in cases decided on the merits. Nor do the authors try to predict the response of the Court to certiorari applications in particular cases. Instead of a dichotomy between cases to be decided for and against a litigant, the cue model is used to dichotomize the percentage of applications that will be granted as opposed to those that will be refused. The key considerations are said to be the presence or absence of the federal government as a party, civil liberty questions, and dissension in the lower courts. Various combinations of these factors were used by the authors to predict the percentage of the certiorari applications studied that would be granted. This work is outside the stream of thought developed by Kort not only for the reasons suggested above but also because of the nonidentification of "legally relevant facts" as cues.

Application of the cue model showed that the presence of three cues gave a prediction of 80 per cent approval as compared to a rate of 70 per cent for party and civil liberties only and 45 per cent for party alone. In Boolean terms, these three relationships would be quite logical in that cases containing party and civil liberties were approved at a higher rate than those containing party alone and cases containing all three had a still higher rate of approval predicted. The same logical relations hold when we examine the total pattern. But since only three of eight patterns led to a prediction rate higher than 50 per cent, most of the cases containing the other five configurations were decided against the petitioner. Since we are not told the number of cases associated with each of the eight patterns, we cannot calculate how many were mispredicted in the sample available. However, the variables used could not account for 7 per cent of the applications granted when no cues were present. Thus contextual-environmental variables may be discovered which will account for Supreme Court decisions on certiorari applications more consistently than this particular model permits.

A third predictive model developed by Fred Kort is an improved version of his initial approach.[15] His focus is still on the decisions of collegial courts in cases decided on their merits and his independent variables are still contextual-environmental stimuli—specifically, the legally relevant facts of the case. Moreover, the assumptions underlying the earlier conceptualization of the judicial decision-making process remain unchanged. But the third model features a normal regression analysis which provides solutions for most of the problems inherent in the earlier work.

Using cases from the United States Supreme Court and the Connecti-

[15] Fred Kort, "Content Analysis of Judicial Opinions and Rules of Law," in Schubert (ed.), *Judicial Decision Making*, pp. 133–97.

cut Supreme Court, Kort identified from 19 to 23 facts in cases involving the right to counsel, involuntary confession, and workmen's compensation. These facts were then scored and put through a multiple regression analysis to determine their approximate numerical weight. A unique characteristic of the process, however, was the method by which the facts were scored. Since a regression analysis of 19 to 23 variables is quite involved, some method of weeding out those that are marginally productive is desirable. One way of doing this is to correlate each variable with a decision for the defendant. A small number of variables with high coefficients could then be chosen for analysis. Kort, however, adopted a standard data-reduction device for this kind of problem; i.e., he put the initial scores through a factor analysis, thereby reducing the number of variables to 5 in the workmen's compensation cases and 9 in each of the other categories.

The next step in the analysis employed the factor loadings to restate the variables in terms of the factors, using a method which reveals "how much of each factor" is present in each case. With the factor estimates as independent variables, the multiple regression analysis provided weights which enabled prediction of the outcome. For the observed value of the dependent variable, Kort used the number of votes in favor of the petitioner or plaintiff. Since the estimated value of the case was obtained by analysis, the prediction was actually in terms of the number of votes cast for the petitioner in a given case. Thus Kort was able to say, "If the correlation between the 'observed values' and the 'estimated values' can be accepted as significant, it can be concluded that the decision of a case, which is represented by the case weight [number of votes predicted for petitioner], is—at a specifiable degree of probability—a function of the combination of factors (the restated combinations of variables)." [16]

Since any observed value of five or more in full decisions of the Supreme Court means victory for the plaintiff, *pro* or *con* outcome could be anticipated on the basis of the number of votes predicted for the petitioner. With that criterion Kort showed a success rate of 88.4 per cent in the involuntary confession cases; 82.9 per cent in the right-to-counsel cases; and 82.3 per cent in the workmen's compensation cases. [17]

---

[16] *Ibid.*, p. 164.

[17] These figures tell us that these two courts have been fairly consistent in the selected subject areas in terms of the facts identified for analysis. When each set of cases was split and the second half predicted from the first, the correlation coefficient between the observed and predicted values was not significant for the involuntary confession cases or the right-to-counsel cases. When prediction backward was attempted, from the second half to the first half of the cases, identical results were obtained. These failures were attributed to the presence of variables in the set of cases

Grunbaum and Newhouse (G-N) have applied a slightly different or Class 4 regression model.[18] Contrary to Kort's assumption that the changing composition of a collegial court does not affect one's ability to predict its decisions, these authors suggest that "the probability of predicting future cases from past cases is limited to particular judges in specific situations. Thus, new personnel and new situations may or may not alter the basic structure utilized for the prediction of a series of cases." [19] Whether it is better to predict the decisions of individual Justices or of the Supreme Court as a whole was determined by correlating the votes from each Justice with each other Justice and factor-analyzing the resulting matrix. Since this produced eight statistically significant factors, it was concluded that each Justice's voting pattern was sufficiently different to warrant analysis of each individual's decisions rather than those of the Court. But since the analysis used all cases in the 1962 term, the authors recognized the possibility that, on occasion, fewer than eight factors might be sufficient. This would be true, for example, if a group of judges all voted the same way in a particular set of cases.

Although facts were identified as independent variables for input to a multiple regression analysis, the Grunbaum-Newhouse model differs from that of Kort in the method of coding the variables and in the use of variables of a political nature. In the latter respect the model is similar to that developed by Tanenhaus.

The G-N model has been applied to twenty Supreme Court cases involving union regulation. In the twenty cases it was found that five of the Justices always voted alike: Warren, Brennan, Harlan, Stewart, and White. Thus only five equations were needed. These equations led to predictive rates of 90 per cent for the five-man majority, 80 per cent for Clark, 70 per cent for Black, 50 per cent for Goldberg, and 40 per cent for Douglas. The importance of the Grunbaum-Newhouse analysis lies in the authors' emphasis on the individual decision as a means of predicting the outputs of collegial courts. Some additional implications of this emphasis are spelled out at a later point in this paper.

predicted which did not appear in the set from which the estimations were obtained. An additional Class 3 model was applied to search-and-seizure cases by the writer in 1963. See "Quantitative Analysis of Judicial Processes: Some Practical and Theoretical Applications," in Baade (ed.), *op. cit.*, pp. 171–74. Comment on this particular application is reserved in view of the extended treatment of discriminant analysis on pages 84–95.

[18] Werner F. Grunbaum and Albert Newhouse, "Quantitative Analysis of Judicial Decisions: Some Problems in Prediction," *Houston Law Review*, III (Fall, 1965), 201–20.

[19] *Ibid.*, p. 202; cf. Lawlor, *op. cit.*, p. 339.

The Psychometric Model

In Class 5 we have a single model, the psychometric, a framework in which the dependent variables are decisions of courts or judges in formal cases.[20] The psychometric is the only model that adopts opinions and attitudes as the independent variables from which decision is to be predicted. This model is an extension of the various applications of Guttmann scales to Supreme Court cases which began in 1959. Initial scaling of these cases was motivated by the desire to investigate certain attitudinal hypotheses and more specifically the question of consensual cognition of the issues presented for decision. In a paper written in 1960 the author used the results of civil liberty scales compiled for 1956–60 to predict the rank order of the Justices on the civil liberty scale for the 1961 term. This prediction held up at the .001 level for the 1961 scale subsequently prepared. But, perhaps more striking, it was affirmed later by a 1961 civil liberty scale prepared independently by Schubert. Schubert also predicted the rank order of the judges on three scales using 1962 cases and is the only person to date who has attempted to predict specific case outcomes by use of the psychometric model.

Unlike those who have predicted the percentage of certiorari decisions to be approved or those who have concentrated on separating decided cases into *pro* and *con* groupings, Schubert forecast the following Supreme Court actions in the area of legislative reapportionment: (1) that in the case of *Beadle v. Scholle* the Court would deny certiorari to the Michigan Supreme Court or affirm that court's decision with Douglas, Black, Goldberg, Warren, and Brennan in the majority; (2) that no *pro* reapportionment decisions of courts other than the Michigan court would be reversed nor would any then docketed antireapportionment decisions be affirmed; and (3) that, viewing *Beadle v. Scholle* as the most "extreme claim of entitlement to political equality" of docketed cases, the voting divisions in other cases would run from 5–4 to 8–1 with Douglas, Black, Goldberg, Warren, and Brennan in the majority and White, Clark, and Stewart joining the majority in that sequence.

Certainly we must marvel at Professor Schubert's courage in making predictions with such specificity. Of all the model builders discussed to this point, none have been so bold as to predict the votes of individual judges in specific cases. Yet precedent can be found in legal circles. In 1962 Fred Rodell, a Yale Law School professor, predicted the vote of the

---

[20] Glendon Schubert, "Prediction from a Psychometric Model," in Schubert (ed.), *Judicial Behavior*, pp. 548–87.

Justices in *Baker v. Carr*.[21] Of the eight votes cast, Rodell forecast seven correctly. This result was accomplished, he tells us, by analyzing the personal or idiosyncratic predilections of each judge. Rodell suggests that such factors as education, temperament, and economic status shape judicial decision-making but the complexity of the ways in which such factors combine to produce choice is said to be beyond "the predictive capacity of even the most intricately attuned and adjusted calculating machine." [22] This amounts to a claim that he, Rodell, has done what an "intricately attuned and adjusted calculating machine" could not.

Be that as it may, Rodell's qualitative approach and Schubert's quantitative effort identify many of the same variables. For Rodell and the judicial behavioralists both emphasize the relationship of human variations to decisional variations. This emphasis contrasts with that of Kort and Nagel, both of whom see less subjectivity in the judicial process. But the difference is one of degree only, since none would deny the effects of such factors on the outputs of the legal system. Schubert and Rodell also agree on the importance placed on judicial attitudes but disagree as to the possibility of systematic and quantitative analysis of those attitudes for predicting court decisions.

How successful is prediction based on attitudes? In regard to Schubert's forecasts for *Beadle v. Scholle*, certiorari was denied as predicted. As for the other two predictions, one case was decided in each category. In both instances the prediction was affirmed. Obviously, there is a measure of success here. But we may inquire, as we did of Rodell, how the result was accomplished. Basically, the forecasts for the reapportionment cases were based upon the following assumptions: (1) that the Justices would vote in the decision of the reapportionment cases "in response to their fundamental attitudes toward civil liberty, and more particularly, to that component of the C scale—the political equality subvariable—to which the reapportionment issue . . . [was] most directly related"; [23] (2) that the most extreme claim of political equality in cases then docketed was present in the case of *Beadle v. Scholle;* (3) that the attitudes of the most liberal members of the Supreme Court were such that extreme claims of political equality were acceptable; and (4) that the most liberal members of the Court were Douglas, Black, Goldberg, Warren, and Brennan.

Schubert's model is obviously superior to Rodell's qualitative approach. Moreover, the application of the model for predicting specific decisions is imaginative. But the limitations of the psychometric ap-

[21] Fred Rodell, "For Every Justice, Judicial Deference Is a Sometime Thing," *Georgetown Law Journal*, L (1962), 700–708.
[22] *Ibid.*, p. 708.   [23] Schubert (ed.), *Judicial Behavior*, p. 578.

proach for forecasting court decisions seem evident. The model is not a rigorous, systematic, and replicative system for relating dependent and independent variables. That judges will vote in terms of attitudes may be tentatively accepted as a working postulate. But the degree of "extremism" attached to the claim in *Beadle v. Scholle* is subjectively determined. That being so, the view that subsequent claims of no greater "extremeness" will be acceptable to certain individuals is difficult to establish. The scalar division between the Justices to whom a claim is acceptable and those to whom it is unacceptable is drawn here prior to decision. In scaling, the ranks of the Justices are determined only after their votes have been cast. This is certainly a difference of some importance.[24]

A Discriminant Function Model

Description

The final model to be discussed here is presented for the first time. Its description and applications will furnish a framework for raising certain questions which, in my opinion, have received inadequate attention previously. The model makes use of the discriminant function, a procedure originated by R. A. Fisher in 1936.[25] A discriminant equation form of the method was initially applied to judicial data in 1963.[26] The discriminant function differs from the normal regression equation in that the criterion to be predicted is a dichotomy. Where regression analysis is normally used to predict one continuous variable from other continuous variables, the discriminant function predicts a dichotomous variable from several numerical variables. We may divide a set of court decisions into two groups and score each group of cases on the same variable. If differences on the variable are correlated with *pro* or *con* decisions, then the means of the scores for each group should differ. If the *pro* cases have the higher mean score and *con* cases the lower, then any case scoring less than the *con* mean will have a higher probability of being a *con* case and

---

[24] Scales may permit us to show that, given a set of civil liberty cases, the votes will differentiate the Justices and that those relative differences will be stable over time. They may enable us to infer that, given a similar set of cases, the relative differences will be maintained. But none of this will allow us to predict in a systematic fashion those cases in which a given judge will vote *pro* defendant and those cases in which he will decide to the contrary.

[25] "The Use of Multiple Measurements in Taxonic Problems," *Annals of Eugenics*, VII (1936), 179–88.

[26] See n. 17.

any case scoring above the *pro* mean will have a higher probability of being a *pro* case.

For cases scoring between the mean values, a certain percentage for each group may overlap. The frequencies for the *con* cases will be declining; those for the *pro* cases increasing. The point at which these frequencies intersect is a critical point or score which guides us in making predictions from scores falling between the two means. For example, consider the following distribution:

Composite Scores

Con *scores*	*Freq.* %	Pro *scores*	*Freq.* %
1	20	3	20
2	30	4	30
3	50	5	50
4	30	6	30
5	20	7	20

The frequency overlap occurs at a score of 4. Beyond that point scores are lower for *con* cases and higher for *pro* cases. Consequently, above the critical point, the ratio of *pro* to *con* cases steadily increases. Below the point, the ratio of *con* to *pro* cases is similarly affected. Thus we would predict *pro* or *con* for an individual case depending upon the relationship of the case score to the critical score.

Now it should be clear that if the difference between the means of the two distributions is sufficiently great and our frequencies are normally distributed, there will be no overlap of scores. In that event the critical score would fall between the tails of the two distributions and perfect prediction would be assured. Our aim is to approximate such an ideal situation as best we can. If each of our cases in each group is scored on several factors, we must weight each factor in such a way that the means of the composite scores differ as much as possible. The discriminant function is a method by which such a result may be obtained. An equation for deriving the discriminant function is required for each factor to be weighted. In a three-variable problem the appropriate equations are:

$$d_1 = a_1 \Sigma X_1^2 + a_2 \Sigma X_1 X_2 + a_3 \Sigma X_1 X_3$$
$$d_2 = \Sigma X_1 X_2 + a_2 \Sigma X_2^2 + a_3 \Sigma X_2 X_3$$
$$d_3 = \Sigma X_1 X_3 + a_2 \Sigma X_2 X_3 + a_3 \Sigma X_3^2$$

where d equals the difference in the means of the two groups on each variable; X equals the score on each variable; and a equals the weights that will maximize the difference in the means of the composite scores.

Methodological Implications

In applying this framework to Supreme Court data it is useful to consider some of its philosophical implications. None of the models discussed here pay much, if any, attention to such problems as the meaning of prediction or the identification of independent and dependent variables, and, in general, the causal or noncausal relations between variables have been ignored.

Consider first the dependence-independence relationship. A correlation between X and Y may indicate a symmetrical relationship—i.e., that a change in X is accompanied by a change in Y and vice versa—or an asymmetrical relation with either X or Y dependent. For purposes of a regression equation, it can simply be decided that the left-hand member of the equation represents the dependent variable. If this is done and a symmetrical relation is assumed, it makes no difference which variable appears on the left. If asymmetry is assumed, however, then we are introducing a temporal sequence—i.e., we are assuming that the change in the dependent variable follows a change in the independent variable but that the opposite relationship does not hold. Schubert is raising a question of symmetry when he asks whether facts control judges or judges facts. Since he opts for the latter, the independent variables for Kort, Nagel, and Grunbaum-Newhouse appear to constitute dependent variables for Schubert. In the application to be presented here, a symmetrical relationship is postulated.

In regard to prediction the matter can be approached in at least two ways. First, prediction may refer to an ability to estimate the decision in a case from knowledge of the scores on a series of quantitative variables. Success may be measured by the improvement in the estimate given the scores over the result that might be attained without them. This would raise no question of cause and effect. It simply asks whether the scores are indicators to the decisions.

On the other hand, prediction may imply that, given cause, we can predict effect. In the first instance the population data are fixed at a point in time. We ask essentially whether some characteristic of the population can be estimated from some other population characteristic. In the second case we have a temporal sequence in which the characteristic that appears first is taken as the cause of some result which follows. But a colligative relation may be established between two elements separated by a temporal sequence without assuming that the first causes the second. For the so-called independent variable may not be the cause of change but merely an indicator of cause. From such a perspective, cause is left undefined and variations in selected indicators are linked to variations in selected subsequent events. In this fashion the differences between attitudes and facts tend to evaporate, since both may be indicators of the same cause.

In the application of the discriminant function described in this paper, prediction is estimation. Our aim is to establish a nexus between two attributes of a population of cases—facts and decisions—without knowledge of "which is the chicken and which is the egg." Although the observation that the circumstances of a case precede its decision is credible, such a time sequence is relevant only in models which determine factual circumstances prior to case decision or from sources other than those in which the decision and the facts are simultaneously reported.

An Application with Data

Since our interest here is in illustrating the model, we have chosen data previously compiled by Fred Kort from majority opinions in Supreme Court cases.[27] Our primary purpose is to compare the results derived from the discriminant function model with those obtained from Kort's regression model using the same data for each comparison.

Adoption of the categories and data developed by Kort neutralizes problems of data relevancy and replication. For if different methods give different results with the same data, the variables associated with the difference must inhere in the methods themselves. Kort attempts to develop a system which will maximize predictive success—i.e., maximize the correlation between the values predicted for the criterion and the values observed on it. The questions raised by our inquiry are whether the discriminant function model will provide a higher rate of successful prediction when applied to the Supreme Court; whether that rate can be improved upon by analyzing individual judges; and, where predictions for individual judges are less successful, whether new variables or new weights can be identified that will improve the individual predictions.

On the basis of Kort's data on involuntary confession and right-to-counsel cases, correlation matrices were factored by elementary factor analysis (EFA) [28] and the resultant factor loadings used as input for the discriminant analysis. This differs from the practice followed with the earlier discriminant equation model, which correlated the facts with decisions for the defendant. It differs also from Kort's estimated factor

---

[27] Complete lists of the cases and the facts are in Kort, "Content Analysis of Judicial Opinions," pp. 137, 138, 140, 142.

[28] See S. Sidney Ulmer, "Toward a Theory of Subgroup Formation in the United States Supreme Court," *Journal of Politics*, XXVII (1965), 133–52.

method. Since the best procedure for scoring the cases is as yet undetermined, experimentation with different methods is desirable. In the procedure used here, if a case has variables 1, 2, 6, 7, and 8 present with variables 1 and 2 loading on factor I and variables 6, 7, and 8 on factor II, then the sum of the loadings of the variables associated with each

Table 4.2. Involuntary confession cases

Factors	Variables No.	f_1	f_2	f_3	f_4	f_5	f_6	f_7	f_8
I	2	.70							
	13	1.00							
II	10		1.00						
	11		.74						
III	6			.01					
	9			.25					
	18			1.00					
	19			.42					
	20			.70					
IV	8				.16				
	14				.62				
	15				1.00				
V	1					.55			
	7					1.00			
	22					.46			
VI	12						1.00		
	17						.53		
VII	3							.51	
	4							.51	
	5							1.00	
VIII	16								1.00
	21								.17

factor respectively can be used to derive the score of a case on that factor.

The elementary factors and the variables associated with them are presented in Table 4.2. As the table shows, EFA loads a variable on a factor in terms of its correlation with a reference variable. In each case the referent is identified by an entry of 1.00. Whereas Kort identified nine factors for 22 variables in the involuntary confession cases and nine factors for 23 variables in the right-to-counsel cases, our procedure identified eight and five factors respectively. Coefficients were computed for each factor and, maintaining relative weights, restated so that the smallest coefficient equaled unity (1).

The eight coefficients for the involuntary confession cases could have been used to predict outcomes for all cases in the population. But our decision rule required that we get the best separation of *pro* and *con* cases with the smallest number of variables.[29]

Given eight factors for 22 variables in the involuntary confession cases, the question was: What combination of factors from this group will maximize the difference between the means of composite scores for our *pro* and *con* groups of cases? A complete answer to this question would have involved the computation of a discriminant function for each possible combination of eight factors or 255 combinations.[30] Since calculations of this sort are quite time-consuming, even for computers, this analysis has not been done. But a step in that direction was made by starting with eight variables and successively eliminating a single variable, recalculating the discriminant function at each step. Thus an equation was calculated using eight factors, seven factors, six factors, and so on. Our choice of the particular combination to be used was made in terms of the probability of misclassifying a particular case with a particular set of variables.[31]

Results of Analysis

When this procedure was carried out for the involuntary confession cases, it was found that four factors provided mean composite scores for the *pro* groups of cases approximately three times that for the *con* group. Table 4.3 gives the detailed results. The same procedure for the right-to-counsel cases produced the five factors identified in Table 4.4.

---

[29] This reflects the value of parsimony often associated with choice among scientific theories. Kort's use of factor analysis to reduce the number of original variables in his cases and the writer's choice of four search-and-seizure variables to predict Court decisions in an earlier study, reflected such a value. But in neither case was the reduction carried out in terms of the best predictors. Indeed, in both cases, there seems to have been a desire to work with fewer variables for computational reasons. The question of the particular combinations of fewer variables that would give best predictive results was raised in the writer's earlier study but not followed up. We do not know whether some smaller combination of factors from Kort's set of nine would give better results than the total number he used or whether fewer than four search-and-seizure variables would do likewise. These considerations led us to raise this general question anew and to attempt an answer.

[30] By the formula $_nC_r = \dfrac{n(n-1)\ \ldots\ (n-r+1)}{r!}$

[31] This probability was computed from the ratio:

$$\frac{D/2}{\sqrt{D/C}}$$

where D is the mean difference of the composite score and C is the number of degrees of freedom of error at any particular step in the analysis.

Table 4.3. Involuntary confession cases

Factor	Coefficient
III	1.94683
IV	1.00000
V	1.01183
VII	2.40861

Probability of Misclassification   .1264882
F Ratio   8.0417929

Computing stepwise discriminant functions for these factors, it was determined that all five gave the best discrimination of our data. The chosen coefficients are presented in Table 4.5. It may be noted that the analysis of the right-to-counsel cases provided weights almost the equivalent of the original scores of 1 and 0. In the involuntary confession cases, on the other hand, factor VII is weighted one and one-half times factor

Table 4.4. Right-to-counsel cases

Factors	Variables No.	f_1	f_2	f_3	f_4	f_5
I	1	.39				
	9	.22				
	15	1.00				
II	5		.60			
	6		1.00			
	7		.84			
	8		.72			
III	20			.49		
	12			.08		
	18			1.00		
IV	14				.44	
	16				.53	
	17				1.00	
	21				.08	
V	2					.44
	3					1.00
	4					.11
	10					.08
	11					.06
	13					.19
	19					−.02
	22					−.19
	23					.36

III and factor III is assigned approximately twice the weight of factors IV and V.

While the relative ranks among the four factors were maintained when all eight were used, the relative weights changed considerably. Thus one must not read the weights as giving the relative importance that the Court attached to a given factor in the total configuration of variables that might have been operative. But if one asks, given a particular set of four factors, how much of the relative variance in the response pattern can be explained by each, the answer is given by analysis of the sum of squares for regression.

It should be noted, also, that while four factors were chosen in one

Table 4.5. Right-to-counsel cases

Factors	Coefficient
I	1.00031
II	1.02197
III	1.13803
IV	1.03518
V	1.00000

Probability of Misclassification .16257672
F Ratio 6.1073549

case and five in another, other groups of factors would have performed almost as well. Thus in the involuntary confession cases correct prediction was expected 87.4 per cent of the time using factors III, IV, V, and VII; 87.1 per cent with III, IV, and VII; and 85.6 per cent with factors III and VII only. In the right-to-counsel cases the probability of misclassification with all factors was a little over .16. But with factor I eliminated, correct prediction would be expected 83 per cent of the time; with factors I and IV eliminated 82 per cent; and with factors I, III, and IV eliminated 79 per cent. The additional computations necessary with more than two factors might impose costs not warranted by the percentage point gains produced in the actual analysis. But that is a question to be answered by the investigator, since only he can determine how much he wishes to spend.

In Table 4.6 are presented the cases from the two sets analyzed in which the observed and predicted outcomes differed. For the involuntary confession cases, the best discrimination was between the 15th and 16th ranks, for the right-to-counsel cases between the 20th and 21st ranks. The discriminant function computed for the first set of cases gave 25 correct predictions out of 26 opportunities, a rate of 96.1 per cent compared to Kort's best rate of 88.4 per cent. For the right-to-counsel cases, a correct assignment was achieved in 32 of 35 cases, 91.4 per cent, as compared with Kort's rate of 82.9 per cent. Thus this particular discriminant function model produced a more effective separation of *pro* and *con* cases in each instance than did Kort's model. It may be noted that in accomplishing this result, the approximately 5-percentage-point spread between Kort's two success rates is maintained between the rates derived with the discriminant function model, the exact difference being that between 5.5 and 4.7. Since in both cases the discrepancy is in the same direction, we surmise that the Court has been more con-

Table 4.6. Cases mispredicted

Number	Rank	Predicted	Observed
Involuntary confession			
8	20	Con	Pro
Right to counsel			
1	23	Con	Pro
8	10	Pro	Con
22	29	Con	Pro

sistent in the involuntary confession cases than in the right-to-counsel cases.[32]

Having successfully predicted *pro* and *con* decisions for two sets of Supreme Court cases, we wished to know whether the level of consistency identified was a product of the choices of all the Justices or a few. If the latter, their identification as well as the identification of the deviants could be instructive. A discriminant function was computed for those Justices who participated in a sufficient number of cases to make analysis possible. This permitted an equation for Justices Frankfurter and Clark in the involuntary confession cases and for Justices Frankfurter, Reed, Jackson, and Burton in the right-to-counsel cases.

[32] Consistent decision-making by a collegial court, of course, may be a function of the inconsistent votes of several Justices. Consider, for example, three consistent Justices who are joined in a five-member majority by alternating pairs of other Justices. If the three are always consistent, the joining pair could be consistent one-third of the time and inconsistent two-thirds of the time with the resulting court decisions always consistent. It would be ironic indeed if impartial justice were accomplished by partial judges, but such a possibility must be recognized. Although Grunbaum and Newhouse have computed regression equations for individual judges and noted differences in the extent to which the same variables predict different judges, they have not gone into the possible consequences of such differentials for the judicial process. Although remarking that the low rate they computed for Douglas suggested the presence of other variables, they did not carry the matter farther.

Our first question was whether the equation for the Court using the same weights would predict equally well for these individual Justices. The Court rates of 96.1 and 91.4 per cent may be compared to the rates presented in column I of Table 4.7. These figures show that the equation of the Court predicted less well for these individuals but still maintained fairly high levels. Using the same weights and factors but recalculating the critical point on the index for each Justice produced the rates in column II. The improvement in the second column reflects the fact that, for each Justice in the right-to-counsel cases, a higher composite score

Table 4.7. Percentage of decisions correctly predicted for individual judges by three procedures

Cases	Decisions by	Procedures		
		I	II	III
Involuntary	Frankfurter	80	84.7	84.7
confession	Clark	85.8	100	
	Supreme Court	96.1		
Right to	Frankfurter	76.5	79.5	82.4
counsel	Reed	81	81.5	81.5
	Jackson	70	75	80
	Burton	77.3	86.4	86.4
	Supreme Court	91.4		

was necessary to produce a *pro* decision. These particular Justices cast a smaller percentage of their votes for the defendant than did the Court as a whole.

In the involuntary confession cases Clark required a higher composite score for a *pro* decision, indicating that he was less favorable to defendants than the Court as a whole. Frankfurter, on the other hand, required a lower score for *pro* classification, revealing a more favorable voting pattern toward defendants. Whether these rates could be improved upon by seeking new combinations of factors or new weights for the same combination for each Justice was the next question. In the case of Clark no improvement was possible. And no new combinations of factors or weights were found that enabled us to predict more successfully for Burton and Reed. On the other hand, by recalculating the weights for the original five factors in terms of Frankfurter's voting splits, we were able to predict 82.4 per cent of his decisions in the right-to-counsel cases. To achieve this slight increase, we assigned disproportionate weight to factors I and IV. This suggests a different emphasis on these factors than that reflected in Court behavior. But even with the improvement, these five factors predicted Frankfurter 9 percentage points less than the level attained for the Court. This may imply that Frankfurter viewed the right-to-counsel cases from a perspective that differed from that of the judges who usually made the majority in the sample cases. The same might be said for Jackson, whose rate was increased 5 percentage points by eliminating factor V and recalculating weights. In Jackson's case the emphasis is on factors I and II, particularly the first.

Some Implications of the Analysis

Perhaps the most striking aspect of the analysis of individual Justices was the high degree to which all were predicted by the use of the Discriminant Function for the Court. Grunbaum and Newhouse did not find this to be true in the labor relations cases, where two of the justices were predicted correctly only 40 and 50 per cent of the time. It would appear that the need for a predictive equation other than that computed for the total group is, in each situation, an empirical question. But this procedure does provide a method of answering those who might maintain that their champion must be analyzed separately from the Court on which he sits.[33] For if a given judge does not behave consistently with the variables which predict Court decision, the procedure used here will so indicate.

As for the three questions that motivated the application of the Discriminant Function, the first has been answered in the affirmative; the model provided better prediction than Kort's regression model. It was not possible to derive an explicit answer to the second query since the data permitted an analysis of only a few of the Justices individually. But the usefulness of individual analysis seems evident; it will merely require working with larger numbers of cases to ensure that the observations in each group exceed the number of variables to be investigated. The third question was answered in the negative for some Justices: prediction of their decisions could not be improved by using new variables and/or weights. For others, the opposite was true. But the search was limited to combinations of the eight and five factors identified earlier. To say that no combination of factors and weights was found in terms of which Reed's decisions were more consistent is not to say (a) that no such factors existed or (b) that though they existed they could not be found. Indeed, if 81.5 per cent correct prediction is unsatis-

---

[33] The writer is currently investigating this problem with regard to the behavior of Frankfurter in civil liberty cases.

factory, then one is challenged to discover variables that would provide a better estimation of that Justice's behavior.

Finally, some emphasis should be placed on the reverse of the question usually posed by models for predicting court decisions. Whereas these models ask: What factors are predictors of decisions? one might ask: Given certain factors that ought to govern decision, what is the relative position of each judge or each court to the ideal of consistency? Having determined the order of judges and courts on such an index, we might then inquire as to the characteristics of those located at different levels. This is to suggest, in other words, that one might have a legitimate interest in getting courts and judges to "follow directions," either from a constitution, a legislature, or the public at large. If so, it is reasonable to ask: Who are the malpracticers? Of course, this assumes that courts and judges have functions to perform and that these functions are determined by others than the judges themselves. If that is so, then the concept of the "maverick judge" may be a viable one.

Visual Representation of Mutual Friendliness

5   Richard L. Merritt*
University of Illinois

THIS paper describes a method useful for the visual representation of time-series data on the attitudes of a set of countries toward one another. The data comprise responses to United States Information Agency surveys over the decade between October, 1954, and February, 1964, of random samples of the French, West German, Italian, and British populations to the question, "What is your opinion of (France, West Germany, Italy, Great Britain, the United States, the Soviet Union)?" [1] The method transforms the underlying shifts in attitudes into three-dimensional vector paths that can be displayed graphically. It rests upon several assumptions.

Interpreting the Question

Changing Predispositions

The question was designed to ascertain the predispositions held by a respondent toward particular countries.[2] The interview situation did not permit him to make an "intellectual" answer. There was no time for

---

* I am indebted to Hayward R. Alker, Jr., of The Massachusetts Institute of Technology, Arnold J. Heidenheimer of the Washington University, and Donald J. Puchala of Columbia University for constructive comments, and to the Yale Political Data Program for research support. Data are from Richard L. Merritt and Donald J. Puchala (eds.), *Western European Perspectives on International Affairs: Public Opinion Studies and Evaluations* (New York: Frederick A. Praeger, 1967).

[1] The question was a part of the regular United States Information Agency surveys in Western Europe. The sampling procedures used in each country remained roughly the same during the entire period under consideration. The Italian data are from October, 1954, to February, 1963, only.

[2] On the measurement of latent dispositions, see Paul F. Lazarsfeld, "A Conceptual Introduction to Latent Structure Analysis," in *Mathematical Thinking in the Social Sciences*, ed. Paul F. Lazarsfeld (Glencoe, Ill.: Free Press, 1954), pp. 349–87; James S. Coleman, *Introduction to Mathematical Sociology* (New York: Macmillan, 1964); and Hayward R. Alker, Jr., "The Comparison of Aggregate Political and Social Data: Potentialities and Problems," *Social Sciences Information*, V (September, 1966), 1–18.

him to dissect his image of a country into its component parts for careful analysis and then to recombine the dissociated aspects into a meaningful, aggregated image on the basis of which he could express his judgment about the country. What was required was an instant judgment. It was likely to be a visceral response: one that might or might not jibe with the response that he would have given if he had had an hour to ponder the question, one that suggested his underlying emotional predispositions about various countries.[3] But since a person's predispositions about an object color his attitudes and behavior toward the object, his first response when asked his opinion of another country may well be his most revealing response.[4] It gives us a ready clue to the larger set of images and attitudes that he may hold regarding the country.

Predispositions change slowly over time. Except in the face of spectacular environmental or personality changes, a person's responses to questions tapping his underlying predispositions are unlikely to shift sharply. In the series of data considered in this paper the most dramatic shift in opinion was toward the Soviet Union between April and November, 1956—a shift that we may reasonably suppose to be due to that country's ruthless suppression of the Hungarian uprising. Yet the downward shift was reversed fairly promptly. Within one or two years, in surveys conducted shortly after the Soviet space exploits in the early

[3] If the respondent were to adopt an intellectual approach, weighing the positive and negative aspects of his image of a country before answering, then we might anticipate that, with increasing education (and hence, presumably, more knowledge about and a richer image of the country in question), he would be more inclined to give an ambivalent response. Close examination of surveys in August, 1955, and June–July, 1961, for the four countries reveals that, in general, the reverse is the case. In the latter survey, the average Western European expression of intense attitudes ("very good" or "very bad" opinions) as a percentage of the total who responded rose slightly from 15 per cent both for respondents with elementary schooling or less and those with the equivalent of a high school education, to 17 per cent for those with at least some university or other advanced education; the percentage of ambivalent responses ("neither good nor bad" opinions) declined on the average from 36 to 33 to 30 per cent for the same groups.

[4] Other possibilities, however, should be considered. First, the issue may be so unimportant for the respondent that he literally has no predisposition toward it; in this case he may respond according to his judgment of the response expected by the interviewer or the response that would be acceptable to some peer group, or he may respond in accord with the latest news report heard over the radio, or even randomly or in some irrational manner. Second, the person may have a predisposition but, for whatever reason, he has trained himself (consciously or unconsciously) to respond to such questions in a way that will not betray this predisposition. Finally, it must be added that knowledge about a person's predispositions may tell us little about his subsequent behavior. An individual may be predisposed to dislike another person but, aware of his basic attitude, may decide to lean over backward to be nice to that person. Alternatively, he may be predisposed to dislike a country, such as the Soviet Union, but be so irritated by the excesses of anti-Communists that he may respond to an interviewer that the Soviet Union "isn't all that bad," or that it has its good points

fall of 1957, positive opinions of the USSR had regained the levels obtaining in the spring of 1956.[5] More important than shifts in opinions reflecting reactions to immediate events—changes that tend to cancel each other out over time anyway—are the long-run developments. It is with such secular shifts in predispositions that this paper is concerned.

Responses of Indifference

The response categories used for the question were changed in the late 1950's. In the surveys from 1954 to 1956 respondents could express a "very good" or "good" opinion of the country in question, a "bad" or "very bad" opinion, or else a "fair" opinion. Beginning in 1956 the middle response category available for those reluctant to express either a good or a bad opinion of the country was a "neither good nor bad" opinion. What difference does this change in wording make in our evaluation of the surveys? Can the responses to earlier surveys be equated with those of later surveys to form a single trend in underlying predispositions?

Going beyond the comparative semantics of this situation, two empirical tests could determine whether or not differences exist in the respondents' understanding of the different response categories—that is, "fair" vs. "neither good nor bad." The first, to my knowledge not yet undertaken, would entail depth interviews of respondents. The second, which the USIA did explore, would be to give the two wordings to comparable samples of the populations in the four countries to see whether or not significantly different sets of responses emerge. In fact, this was the case only in Great Britain, where, in seven cases with such "split samples," four had response differences significant at the .10 level or better. In France, with seven split samples, none produced significantly different responses; and only one did so in both West Germany (with eight chances) and in Italy (with nine chances). This suggests that for our purposes it is fair to equate the responses of both the earlier and the later surveys. The possibility of noncomparability, however, particularly in the case of Great Britain, should be borne in mind.[6]

More important from a substantive point of view is the question of

[5] For further discussion of this point, see Karl W. Deutsch and Richard L. Merritt, "The Effects of Events upon National and International Images," in *International Political Behavior: A Social-psychological Approach*, ed. Herbert C. Kelman (New York: Holt, Rinehart, Winston, 1965), pp. 132–87.

[6] I cannot explain why Great Britain should be an exception in this regard. The answer does not seem to lie in the translations of the response categories, since these are quite literal in each case: *opinion moyenne* vs. *ni bonne ni mauvaise* in France, *mittelmässige* vs. *weder gute noch schlechte* in West Germany, and *discreta* vs. *nè buona nè cattiva* in Italy.

what either response really means. What do we know when a respondent says that his opinion of a particular country is "fair" or "neither good nor bad"? On the one hand, such a response may be the considered opinion of the interviewee who is trying to rate all countries according to a five-point scale ranging from +2 (= "very good") through ±0 (= "fair" or "neither good nor bad") to −2 (= "very bad"). On the other hand, we can easily imagine it to be a response of indifference, given by those who do not know or do not care but who, for whatever reason, prefer not to respond "I don't know" to an interviewer.[7] The fact that respondents who have a "fair" opinion of one country tend also to have a "fair" opinion of other countries[8] supports the latter line of reasoning. In this paper I shall assume that "fair" and "neither/nor" opinions are responses of indifference and, for the purposes of scaling, shall treat them as equivalent to "don't know" answers by interviewees.

The Intensity of Predispositions

For the person whose opinion of a particular country is favorable, there are two possible response categories: that he has a "good" opinion of the country or that his opinion is "very good." How can we evaluate these for the purpose of scaling? In some cases it is sufficient merely to lump the two categories together to get the total number of favorable responses. A weighting system, however, taking into account differing levels of intensity among respondents would be preferable.

In this paper I shall use an *equal-interval scale*, assigning to a "very good" opinion double the weight of a "good" opinion. A "very bad" opinion by the same token will receive double the weight of a "bad" opinion. It must be stressed that the assumption implicit in this decision is not based on empirical evidence.

Two points are important here. First, weighting systems used to gauge the intensity of opinions will vary from individual to individual, from country to country. To equate them or to assume that they have the

[7] Responses of "don't know" are also troublesome. They may indicate an unwillingness to respond, or insufficient information upon which to base a response, or indecision due to cross-pressures. Much theoretical and empirical work remains to be done on this aspect of the salience of perceptions. See also Donald J. Puchala's treatment of this problem in Merritt and Puchala (eds.), *op. cit.*, chap. viii.

[8] Looking at the April, 1956, survey in France, for instance, and at the paired responses of Frenchmen to questions about West Germany, Great Britain, the United States, and the Soviet Union, it turns out that an average of 48 per cent of those responding "fair" to one country gave the same response to another (an average of 32 per cent of the entire sample of 800 respondents gave "fair" responses). Seventy per cent of those responding either "fair" or "don't know" to one country (an average of 57 per cent of the entire sample) gave one or the other of these responses to another country.

same basis is, without question, a distortion of reality. At the present
time, however, we do not have adequate information about this reality,
about the differing weighting systems of individual respondents. Conceivably such information could be secured through depth interviews.
Further experimentation with the USIA and other data could study the
effects of different weighting schemes, such as assigning "very good"
opinions a score three or four or even ten times as great as that assigned
to "good" opinions.[9]

Second, some respondents doubtless have unimodal patterns of thinking, in which opinions cluster around the middle of a scaled set of responses and few opinions are extreme, whereas others have bimodal
patterns of thinking. The latter would be inclined to express either "very
good" or "very bad" opinions of countries and to ignore in their responses
any gradations of gray between the two extremes. In both cases an equal-
interval scale might belie reality: for the unimodal thinker a rating of
"very good," which would seldom be awarded any country, would weigh
far more heavily in his mind than twice the weight of a "good" rating;
and, for the bimodal thinker, a change in opinion from a neutral or indifferent response to a "good" opinion might well be greater than the
jump from "good" to "very good." Having made the decision about
direction, he may be quite willing to jump immediately to high levels of
intensity, to throw the entire force of his thinking behind his initial decision about direction. Additional research based on the USIA data could
usefully determine the distribution and demographic characteristics of
such unimodal and bimodal "respondent types."

Vectors of Predispositions

Scaling Direction and Salience

When we look at data about the opinion of a population toward another
country, three aspects are crucial: first, the direction of the opinion, that
is, whether it is predominantly favorable or unfavorable; second, the
extent to which the country in question is sufficiently important for the
interviewees to have a firm opinion about it; and, third, changes in
opinion over time. No single scale that I know of can accommodate these
three aspects simultaneously. Constructing separate scales for changes

---

[9] On this point see Robert P. Abelson and John W. Tukey, "Efficient Conversion
of Non-metric Information into Metric Information," *Proceedings of the Social
Statistics Section, 1959* (Washington, D.C.: American Statistical Association, 1960),
pp. 226–30.

in direction over time and changes in salience over time simplifies the problem. These scales can then be combined by graphic means.

Some abbreviations will facilitate our discussion of these scales. It will be recalled that five possible responses were open to interviewees:

VGO = Very good opinion of the country in question
GO = Good opinion
FO = Fair opinion; neither good nor bad opinion
BO = Bad opinion
VBO = Very bad opinion

A sixth, albeit implicit, response category that the interviewee could choose was:

DK = Don't know; refused to answer

The total opinion score, T, accounts for 100 per cent of the responses in a survey:

$$T = VGO + GO + FO + BO + VBO + DK$$

In the foregoing paragraphs I indicated that intense responses ("very good" or "very bad" opinions) would be assigned a weight twice as great as that assigned to milder responses ("good" or "bad" opinions); and that "fair opinion" and "don't know" responses would be treated as a single category of indifference. Therefore:

$G = 2(VGO) + GO$ (positive opinion score)
$B = BO + 2(VBO)$ (negative opinion score)
$I = FO + DK$ (indifference opinion score)

If our sole task were to describe the direction of attitudes over time, then a simple bias index would serve the purpose. The friendliness (F) score of a population toward another country would be its positive opinion score divided by the sum of its positive and negative opinion scores:

(1)
$$F = \frac{G}{G + B} .$$

If 2 per cent of the respondents in country x express a "very good" opinion of country z and 46 per cent a "good" opinion ($G = (2 \times 2) + 46 = 50$), and 39 per cent have a "bad" opinion with another 3 per cent having a "very bad" opinion ($B = 39 + (3 \times 2) = 45$), then:

$$F_x = \frac{50}{50 + 45} = .53.$$

This index of $F_x = .53$ says that 53 per cent of the combined opinion score (positive + negative) was positive. And it can be seen that, using this index, friendliness scores can range between .00 (when no respondent with a firm opinion is positively inclined toward the country in question) and 1.00 (when all respondents with firm opinions are positively inclined toward the country).

This paper, for ease of graphic representation, will use the friendliness index in a slightly different form:

$$(2) \qquad\qquad F = \frac{G - B}{G + B}.$$

This formula merely transforms the friendliness scores in a linear manner, ranging them from -1.00 (all firm opinions are negative) through $\pm.00$ (the "break-even" point, at which half of the combined opinion score is positive, half negative) to $+1.00$ (all firm opinions are positive), but without changing the relationship among them. To use the example from above:

$$F_x = \frac{50 - 45}{50 + 45} = \frac{5}{95} = +.05.$$

It will be noted that, in this example, 90 per cent of the sample in country x expressed a firm opinion about country z. Suppose we consider another example, however, in which 3 per cent of the respondents in country y have "very good" opinions and 4 per cent "good" opinions of country z $(G = (3 \times 2) + 4 = 10)$, and 3 per cent have "bad" opinions and another 3 per cent "very bad" opinions $(B = 3 + (3 \times 2) = 9)$. In this case, in which only 13 per cent of the total sample had firm opinions, the friendliness score is again:

$$F_y = \frac{10 - 9}{10 + 9} = \frac{1}{19} = +.05.$$

Although, to be sure, the direction of attitudes toward z in both x and y is of the same magnitude $(F = +.05)$, it would be rash to conclude that the two populations share truly comparable predispositions toward country z. Nine of ten respondents in country x have firm opinions, in contrast to the one in eight with a firm opinion in country y. It is important, then, to find a way to indicate differential levels of salience.

The most convenient index of salience is the percentage of respondents who answer a question with firm opinions. With the notation above, the formula for this index would be:

$$(3) \qquad\qquad S = \frac{VGO + GO + BO + VBO}{T} = \frac{T - I}{T}.$$

Again, however, this index produces scores ranging from .00 (when no respondent has a firm opinion) to 1.00 (when all respondents have firm opinions). When revised by means of a linear transformation so that the index ranges between -1.00 and $+1.00$, thereby facilitating graphic representation and making it comparable to the friendliness index, the formula is: [10]

(4)
$$S = \frac{T - 2I}{T}.$$

The levels of indifference in the two examples used above are 10 per cent and 87 per cent, respectively, producing salience scores of

$$S_x = \frac{100 - 2(10)}{100} = \frac{80}{100} = +.80$$

and

$$S_y = \frac{100 - 2(87)}{100} = \frac{-74}{100} = -.74.$$

This formula makes clear the fact that country z was immensely more important in the mind of respondents in country x than in country y. But, unless used in conjunction with friendliness scores, salience scores tell us little more than this.

Temporal Trends in Friendship and Salience

For each point in time at which a survey was taken, then, we can determine both the direction and salience of a population's predisposition toward another country. Table 5.1 shows the changing French view of West Germany from 1954 to 1964, including the raw data (raw marginal frequency distributions) upon which the calculations are based as well as the friendliness and salience scores. But how can we use these data?

One of the more phenomenal events of the postwar world has been the extent to which France and Germany, traditional enemies for at least a century, have been able to create far-reaching plans and institutions for cooperation. A key question among those watching this development is the extent to which such steps reflect or influence relations at a lower level. Has the supposedly long-standing hostility between Frenchmen and Germans given way to a new era of friendship? A glance at the data in Table 5.1. suggests that this is certainly the case as far as the French are concerned (and the same is true, as we shall see later, of the West German image of France). In October, 1954, shortly after the French

[10] Since we are dealing with percentages rather than raw data, in effect this formula is: $S = T - 2I$, when $T = 1.00$ and I is some fraction of T.

Table 5.1. The French attitude toward West Germany, October, 1954, to February, 1964 *

Date	No. of month	Distribution of responses						Opinion scores			Friend-liness	Sali-ence
		VGO	GO	FO	BO	VBO	DK	G	B	I		
Oct 1954	1	1%	8%	23%	22%	9%	37%	10	40	60	−.60	−.20
Feb 1955	5	1	12	28	19	7	33	14	33	61	−.40	−.22
Jun 1955	9	1	9	29	22	5	34	11	32	63	−.48	−.26
Aug 1955	11	—	13	33	22	6	26	13	34	59	−.44	−.18
Dec 1955	15	1	10	36	21	6	26	12	33	62	−.46	−.24
Apr 1956	19	2	10	31	23	8	26	14	39	57	−.48	−.14
May 1957 †	32	2	19	29	15	3	32	23	21	61	+.04	−.22
Nov 1957	38	3	20	32	12	3	30	26	18	62	+.18	−.24
Oct 1958	49	6	31	28	7	1	27	43	9	55	+.66	−.10
Feb 1960	65	3	30	32	9	3	23	36	15	55	+.42	−.10
Jun 1961	81	4	26	32	14	5	19	34	24	51	+.18	−.02
Jun 1962	93	3	31	35	10	3	18	37	16	53	+.40	−.06
Feb 1963	101	6	33	37	11	2	11	45	15	48	+.50	+.04
Feb 1964	113	12	41	30	7	2	8	65	11	38	+.72	+.24

* See the text for explanations of the abbreviations and formulas for friendliness and salience scores. Data are from Richard L. Merritt and Donald J. Puchala, eds., *Western European Perspectives on International Affairs: Public Opinion Studies and Evaluations* (New York: Frederick A. Praeger, 1967).

† Data from two surveys in May, 1957, have been combined.

parliament vetoed a plan for military integration under the European Defense Community, more than three French respondents expressed negative opinions of West Germany for every one who had a positive opinion. By 1964 these figures had more than reversed themselves. The ratio of positive to negative opinions was almost six to one. Meanwhile the percentage of those with firm opinions rose from 40 to 62, suggesting that the salience of the French image of West Germany increased along with the friendliness of that image.

The changes in French predispositions toward West Germany from one polling date to the next are shown in Figure 5.1. An advantage of such "fever curves" is that they can be related easily to other events and processes. If we have other indications of trends toward or away from European integration—such as trade flow, press attitudes, institutional developments, or elite attitudes over time [11]—we can trace their relationship to trends in public opinion. Did rising French popular friendship toward West Germany precede or follow other indicators of integration, or were these trends simultaneous or even contradictory or unrelated? A disadvantage of "fever curves" is that their many up-and-down movements frequently create "noise" that drowns out the underlying trend existing in the data. Although this is not particularly problematic for the data presented in Figure 5.1, for other data considered in this paper it is a serious disadvantage.

Sometimes it is precisely the underlying or secular trend—and not the short-term oscillations—that interests us. For one thing it would give us a clear picture of the direction and over-all extent of change from 1954 to 1964 in the friendliness and salience of the French image of West Germany. For another it would enable us to calculate the average change for each unit of time (month). This in turn gives us a measuring rod against which to compare the actual developments in the French image and, what is more important for our purposes, a means to compare image changes from one country to the next.[12] Conceivably it would also be possible to determine the extent to which movements in certain directions are associated with integrative trends, thereby enabling the secular

---

[11] See the findings reported in Part III of Karl W. Deutsch, Lewis J. Edinger, Roy C. Macridis, and Richard L. Merritt, *France, Germany and the Western Alliance: A Study of Elite Attitudes on European Integration and World Politics* (New York: Scribner's, 1967), pp. 218–64.

[12] If the trend line fits closely enough and if we assume that the conditions that gave rise to it will continue unchanged, then we can predict (within certain confidence intervals) future developments in predispositions; alternatively, if we can isolate the conditions that influence the secular trend, we can make contingency predictions of future developments. The purpose of this paper, however, is to develop a descriptive rather than a predictive instrument.

trends in images to serve as indicators of progress toward or away from political integration.

The simplest trend line is a *linear regression*. Resting upon the statistical method of "least squares," it is the best-fitting straight line describing the data in all their variations. The standard formula for this is:

(5) $y = a + bt$

where, in our case, y is the level of friendliness or salience, t is the time dimension measured in months (1 = October, 1954, to 113 = February, 1964), a is the height of the trend line on the vertical axis at $t = 0$, and b is the average monthly change in y. For French predispositions toward West Germany, these regression coefficients are:

$$y_F = -.474 + .01088t \quad (r = .88, \; r^2 = .77)$$

and

$$y_S = -.263 + .00314t \quad (r = .88, \; r^2 = .78)$$

A trend line based on these calculations would show that French friendliness toward West Germany, which in October, 1954, stood at the $-.46$ level, had risen by February 1964 to $+.76$; meanwhile the salience of this French image increased from $-.26$ to $+.09$. These linear trend lines are shown in Figure 5.1.

A somewhat more complicated trend line is a second-order curve or parabola. It reduces a set of data (such as friendliness scores over time) to a single line with a fixed arc. In some cases second-order curves would

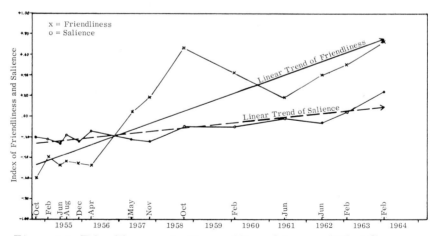

Figure 5.1. Friendliness and salience of French image of West Germany, October, 1954, to February, 1964

have described our data better than do linear regressions (or first-order curves), in the sense of explaining more of the variance in these data. In what follows, however, I have relied solely upon linear regressions, sacrificing the closeness of fit that second-order (or even higher-order) curves occasionally produced. The reason for this lies in a characteristic of second-order curves that emerged in experiments with the graphic representation of the USIA data. Such curves, even when they fit the data better over all, tend to distort the initial and ultimate points of the trend line more than do linear regressions. For some purposes second-order curves would be more appropriate; for the vector paths to be discussed in this paper they seemed less so.[13]

Another possibility should be mentioned. The data for the entire decade could be broken into two approximately equal periods and separate linear trend lines constructed for each period. This would serve to make the trends more dynamic and even to show an element of curvilinearity. Such a broken linear regression would reveal, for example, a low but fairly constant level of friendship toward the Soviet Union during the period from October, 1954, to October, 1958, followed by a sharply rising trend in the second period from November, 1959, to February 1964. A similar analysis of French friendliness toward West Germany would show that most of the growing warmth occurred during the first half of the decade from 1954 to 1964. The utility of this method, however, will not be explored in this paper, which concentrates upon secular trends for the period as a whole.

Plotting Trends in Friendliness and Salience

The two dimensions of friendliness and salience can be plotted on a plane graph, with friendliness as the horizontal axis (with scores ranging from -1.00 to $+1.00$) and salience as the vertical axis (again with scores ranging from -1.00 to $+1.00$). This *predispositional field* for a population's image of other countries is shown in Figure 5.2. For each point in time the intersect of a population's friendliness and salience scores vis-à-vis another country could be located on this field. In the first (northeast) quadrant would be those intersects in which both the friendliness and the salience scores are positive; the second (southeast) quadrant would contain intersects of positive friendliness scores and negative salience scores; the third (southwest) quadrant, negative friendliness and salience scores; and the fourth (northwest) quadrant, negative friendliness and positive salience scores. The data in Table 5.1 show that the French

---

[13] I am indebted to Stephen C. Stephens of the University of California at Los Angeles for his enlightening discussion of these points.

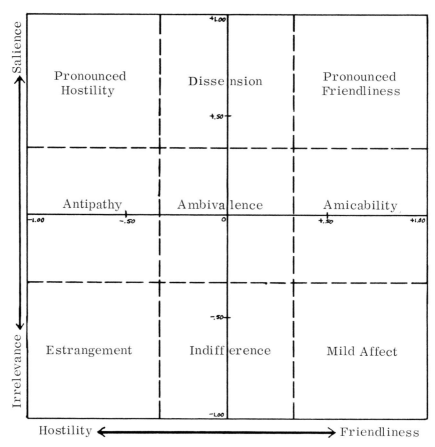

Figure 5.2. Predispositional field

image of West Germany in 1954 was in the third quadrant; by 1957 it was located in the second quadrant; and not until 1963 did it move into the first quadrant.

In Figure 5.2, however, the entire friendliness-salience predispositional field is divided into nine equal areas, each given a label more or less characterizing the type of attitude appropriate to it.[14] An intersect in the

---

[14] The field, of course, could be subdivided in many other ways as well. Its division into nine equal areas gives us more flexibility in characterizing the nature of certain types of intersects—and particularly to permit bands of ambivalence or neutrality between outright hostility and friendliness and between high salience and irrelevance —without creating an unmanageable number of areas. In subsequent figures format considerations have led to the presentation of graphs in which portions without data were cut off. They should be interpreted as ranging from −1.00 to +1.00 on both axes.

northwest corner of the field would indicate that, at a given time, at least two-thirds of the population expressed its predisposition toward a country and the bulk of these expressions (that is, at least two-thirds of the combined opinion score) was negative. Such a situation of negative consensus I have termed "pronounced hostility." "Dissension" suggests a situation in which most of the respondents have opinions about the country in question but are sharply divided in their evaluation of that country; "pronounced friendliness" a condition of consensus on positive attitudes toward the country; "antipathy" a situation in which roughly half of the population has an opinion and these opinions are predominantly negative; and so forth. It should be stressed that the labels refer *solely* to the aggregate predispositions of a population toward a particular country and not to any more generalized characteristic of that population. Viewed in these terms, the French image of Germany shifted from "antipathy" in 1954 to "ambivalence" in 1957 and then to "amicability" as early as October, 1958. These shifts are shown on a two-dimensional field in Figure 5.3.

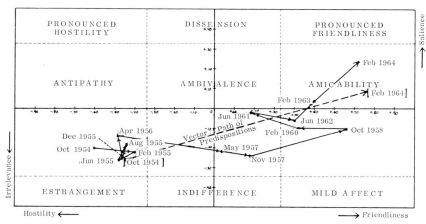

Figure 5.3. French predispositions toward West Germany, October, 1954, to February, 1964

The broken line in Figure 5.3 is what I shall call the French *vector path of predispositions* toward West Germany. This vector path represents a *combined index of change over time in friendliness and salience*. It merely connects the intersects of friendliness and salience levels at the initial survey in October, 1954 (according to the linear regression model), and at the last polling in February, 1964. The vector path itself is by no means a linear regression on the individual intersects plotted in Figure 5.3. A visual comparison of the vector path and the solid line connecting the individual intersects nonetheless suggests that the fit is close.[15]

The vector path of predisposition, although plotted on a two-dimensional field in Figure 5.3, also expresses the third dimension of time. It would be possible to present the data more accurately in a three-dimensional field, in which the time axis would be perpendicular to the friendliness and salience axes. The vector of French predispositions toward Germany would in such a case extend 113 units (months) into this third dimension (that is, toward or away from the eye). Since, however, the time period for almost all the data presented in this paper is the same—from October, 1954, to February, 1964—I have not added the third dimension in the figures that follow. For data with varying time periods this would not only be possible but essential.[16]

Vector paths of predispositions were plotted for the changing image of French, West German, Italian, and British respondents not only toward each other but also toward the United States and the Soviet Union. In the ensuing section, however, only a few of these vector paths will be presented and their relevance for empirical political research discussed. It should not be necessary to stress the fact that in this section we are dealing with *mass predispositions*, not official policy developments. The relationship between the two is nonetheless striking enough in some cases for it to cry out for more extensive analysis.

Vector Paths of Friendliness and World Politics

Patterns of Attitude Change

Let us first turn to some general characteristics of the data. One point of interest emerges if we plot on a scattergram the intersects of the friendliness and salience indexes for each population's predispositions

[15] In a sense this vector path may be viewed as an "average regression line." It should be added, however, that not all the vector paths follow the two sets of data as closely as that shown in Figure 5.3. On vector analysis in general, see Hugh G. Campbell, *Introduction to Matrices, Vectors, and Linear Programming* (New York: Appleton-Century-Crofts, 1965).

[16] If we assume that there is equal variance on the two axes—an assumption that still needs considerable examination—then it is also possible to compute the angles and geometric lengths of each vector path. These are useful both (a) for hypotheses about the consequences of the direction of vector paths on the predispositional field and (b) for specifying the degree of the angle between the vectors of the two countries' predispositions toward each other, as well as (c) for comparing over-all movements of vector paths (e.g., the average length of the vector paths discussed in this paper is .37, but the length of the predispositional vector path of the French image of West Germany is 1.27 and that of the German image of France 1.32; vector paths of predispositions toward the United States and the Soviet Union—at the extremes of the friendliness axis—are smallest, averaging .27 and .28 respectively).

toward every other country at each polling (Figure 5.4). The best-fitting curve for these data is a parabola or second-order curve, high in salience at both ends of the friendliness scale and low in salience around the break-even point in terms of friendliness (that is, $F = \pm.00$, the point at which half of the combined opinion score is positive, half negative). In part the nature of the curve is determined by the scaling system used in this paper. Responses of "fair opinion" and "neither good nor bad

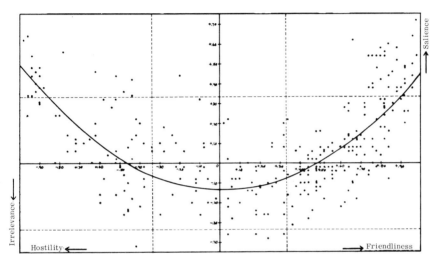

Figure 5.4. The distribution of Western European friendliness and salience intersects, for the entire period from October, 1954, to February, 1964

opinion," it will be recalled, are treated as indications of indifference on the part of the respondent. The curve is nonetheless useful for demonstrating two aspects of processes of opinion formation and change.

First, the parabola suggests that there is a high degree of association between consensus within a population regarding the direction of a predisposition toward a country and the salience of the predisposition itself. Sharp division about direction is characterized by respondents' retreat into answers of indifference. Only one of the 294 intersects shown in Figure 5.4—in October, 1958, when the Italian sample rated the Soviet Union $+.44$ in salience and $-.20$ in friendliness—fell into that portion of the graph labeled "dissension," that range within which attitudes are both highly salient and fairly evenly divided between the advocates and the detractors of a particular country. Similarly, only in October, 1954, when the British sample scored $-.42$ both in salience and direction of predisposition toward Italy, did an intersect fall into the range of attitudes labeled "estrangement." Evidently, few Britishers cared enough about Italy to have firm opinions about that land, and most of those did have opinions viewed Italy negatively. No intersects whatsoever are in the "mild affect" category, an attitude that we might guess would characterize the American image of Monaco, about which few people know enough to have opinions but toward which those with opinions are more likely than not to feel positively.

Second, and implicit in the first point, when a population is changing its collective predisposition toward another country from negative to positive (or vice versa), the salience of that predisposition drops off as the level of friendliness approaches the break-even point and then rises again as the other pole is approached. Viewed in another way, a population's aggregate attitudes toward other countries are unimodal rather than bimodal.[17] But how valid is this generalization for all countries and all times? The data discussed here pertain to countries and times in which there was considerable domestic consensus about the external environment. It would be interesting to have comparable data for Germany in 1932, when, according to the history books, the German image of the Soviet Union was sufficiently salient and bimodal for it to contribute to the numerous outbreaks of street fighting between more and less organized Nazi and Communist gangs. It is clearly, however, a testable proposition that deserves further investigation.[18]

[17] Earlier, when discussing the assumption underlying my weighting of the intensity of predispositions, I suggested that *individual* attitudes could be unimodal or bimodal. Here we are talking about the unimodality of *collective* attitudes. In their predispositions toward other countries most of the people cluster around the category of indifferent or undecided responses, with the number of "good" and "bad" responses somewhat smaller, and the number of "very good" and "very bad" responses smaller yet. Toward any particular country the modal category may be skewed toward the "good" or the "bad" side of the continuum. In changing their opinions, most people do not jump immediately from a "good" to a "bad" opinion but rather go through a phase of cross-pressure and indecision. Much literature exists on this subject, both as it pertains to individual and to collective behavior. Some examples include Louis Guttmann, "A New Approach to Factor Analysis: The Radex," in *Mathematical Thinking in the Social Sciences*, ed. Paul F. Lazarsfeld (Glencoe, Ill.: Free Press, 1954), pp. 258–348; Hayward R. Alker, Jr., and Bruce M. Russett, *World Politics in the General Assembly* (New Haven and London: Yale University Press, 1965); and Richard L. Merritt, *Symbols of American Community, 1735–1775* (New Haven and London: Yale University Press, 1966).

[18] Important differences characterize the four countries. The British and French curves (not shown in this paper) are the deepest, epitomizing the above proposition about the association between domestic consensus on the direction of predispositions and the salience of those predispositions. The difference is that the British curve is skewed somewhat toward the friendliness pole, the French curve somewhat toward the hostility pole. The Italian curve, by way of contrast, is flatter than the others, suggesting a greater tolerance of ambiguity among Italians or else reflecting the potentially disruptive dissension in Italian images of the international environment. West Germans, more than other Europeans, are inclined toward extremes, viewing other countries either quite positively or quite negatively: indeed, only 9 of 69 (or 13 per cent) of the German predispositional intersects fall into the area of "ambivalence."

It may be added that, in general, the longitudinal data discussed in following sections of this paper behave in the manner postulated here on the basis of a cross-sectional reading of the data. The vector paths shown in the following figures are close to the parabola depicted in Figure 5.4.

The Propensity to Like and Be Liked

Another way to approach general differences in Western European perspectives is to consider each population's cumulative predispositions toward other countries. Here we are interested in each European population's view of the other three Western European countries as well as the United States and the Soviet Union; the average of these four sets of images can then be considered as a general Western European predisposition toward other countries. These cumulated averages are shown graphically in Figure 5.5. At this point, however, I shall merely note some

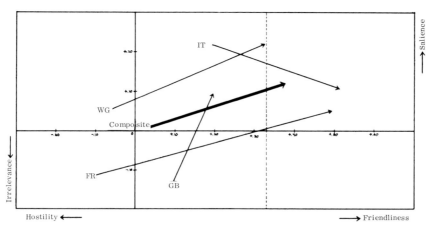

Figure 5.5. Cumulative Western European ⌈predispositions toward friendliness

of the trends in amicability, leaving interpretations of these trends for later.

The over-all climate of Western European predispositions (the "composite" vector path in Figure 5.5) improved considerably, from almost the midpoint of ambivalence in 1954 to an atmosphere of outright amicability by 1964. This general trend held true for each of the four countries, albeit with some differences: the average shift was most marked in France, was not much different from the composite average in both West Germany and Italy, and was least noticeable in Great Britain. By 1964 France and Italy had moved from ambivalent to amicable positions, and Germany had almost crossed the same imaginary bar-

rier. Images of foreign countries also became more salient over time in
all countries except Italy. Among Italians the salience of the predispositions toward each country dropped off during the course of the decade
between 1954 and 1964.

This climate of increasing warmth reappears if we turn these data
around to examine the cumulative Western European image of each of
the six countries (Figure 5.6). Interestingly enough, it is Italy that is the
primary recipient of the growing amicability of Western Europeans: the
length of the vector path describing Italy's popularity is almost twice as
long as the average of the vector paths for the other five countries. Moreover, except for the image of the Soviet Union, these vector paths all
increased in salience. The direction and salience of the vector paths,
taken together, seem to confirm the general pattern of attitude change
discussed in the previous section.

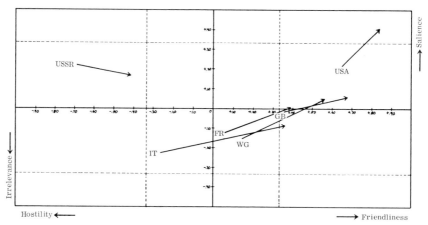

Figure 5.6. Cumulative Western European predispositions toward six
countries

Figure 5.6 also suggests another proposition about aggregated popular
attitudes toward other countries (and, indeed, toward practically any
other event): greater shifts in predispositions occur in the middle ranges
of the friendliness scale than at either extreme. In other words, images
upon which there is considerable consensus, whatever the level of salience, are more stable than those upon which the sampled population is
divided. Data on predispositions toward America point to a corollary
proposition: there is a "natural limit" to movement in either direction
away from the center of the range. At a first glance the image of the
United States seems to suffer in contrast to those of other countries.

Western European friendliness toward America increased .19 from 1954 to 1964, whereas the average of the images of the other five countries increased by .40—more than twice as much! This apparent discrepancy is doubtless due to the position of the United States on the scale as a whole. When an image is at either end of the spectrum and moving toward a more extreme position, additional increments are increasingly smaller. Data on predispositions toward Russia indicate that movement from an extreme position toward the center of the range may proceed with ever greater increments.

Views of Superpowers

Western European predispositions toward the United States and the Soviet Union from 1954 to 1964 were bifurcated (Figure 5.7). The atti-

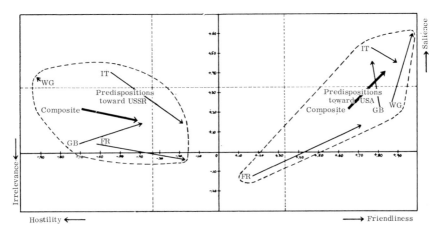

Figure 5.7. Attitudes toward the Soviet Union and the United States

tude toward America was highly friendly and, except in the case of France, quite salient. America's best friend in Europe is clearly West Germany. By 1964, 88 per cent of the West Germans had a definite opinion about the United States, and 99 per cent of these respondents had a "good" or "very good" opinion of America. In marked contrast to official relations, French public attitudes toward America increased considerably in warmth during the course of the decade. Even so, by 1964 the French were neither so interested in nor so friendly toward the United States as the other three countries had been as early as 1954. Only in Great Britain did the level of friendliness diminish, despite increasing salience. If this shift had been dramatic, we might attribute it to increasing popular

disillusionment among Britishers about the United States, and even begin to worry about the effect that this development might have on general Anglo-American relations. In fact, however, the shift was slight—
amounting to .04 on the friendliness scale—and, in terms of the *actual
number* of English respondents holding favorable images of the United
States, more than offset by the increased salience of the over-all image
(that is, the absolute number of English respondents viewing the United
States favorably increased). By no means do these figures suggest mas-
sive damage to the American image in Britain.

Favorable views of the Soviet Union increased markedly in Western
Europe. (And looking at the data, one suspects that, had not the Hungarian crisis of 1956 intervened, favorable attitudes toward the Soviet
Union would have increased even more dramatically.) Only in West
Germany did predispositions toward Russia become slightly more salient
and negative. For the other three countries the average level of friendliness increased by .37, with the French most inclined to view the USSR
with increasing favor. (Incidentally, the vector paths shown on Figure
5.7 provide an excellent example of the relative stability of predispositions at the extremes of the friendliness scale and of the limits of movement toward the extremes.)

What these data indicate is that the publics in Western Europe are
inclining ever more toward a détente with the Soviet Union, albeit not at
the expense of their ties to America. On the one hand, they appear to
have made up their minds about the United States. Predispositions are
neither friendlier nor more salient toward any other country, as may be
seen in Figure 5.6. It would doubtless take a major disaster in world
politics to reverse this trend in any significant manner. On the other
hand, Western Europeans seem to be in the process of changing their
minds about the Soviet Union, becoming less willing to express outright
hostility or even antipathy and more inclined to view the country with
ambivalence. Only West Germany is an exception: from 1954 to 1964
West German poll respondents became increasingly firm in their positive
opinions of the United States and remained almost static in their negative
predispositions toward Russia. If these data can be viewed in Cold War
terms, Germans are moving in a different direction than are the remainder of the major Western European peoples. They seem to be pushing
somewhat toward greater tension at a time when the French, Italians,
and British appear to be stressing relaxation. One explanation for this
may be that West Germans, who experienced at first hand in 1945 the
full force of the Red Army, are particularly cognizant of the potential
danger of a Soviet military establishment equipped with missiles and
nuclear warheads; another may be that West Germans perceive the

maintenance of some East-West tension as an appropriate way to ensure American support for Germany in the new Europe.

The European Community

Within Western Europe, as may be seen in Figure 5.8 the level of friendliness among France, West Germany, and Italy increased from 1954 to

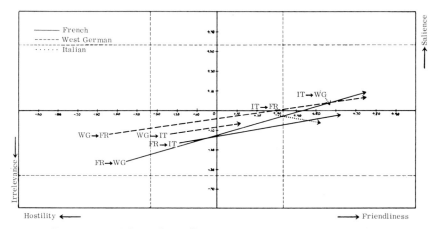

Figure 5.8. Mutual predispositions among EEC members

1964.[19] What is particularly striking is the relationship between France and West Germany. In the earlier period both countries were relatively unfriendly toward one another, and the level of salience of these predispositions was relatively low. By 1964, a year after the Franco-German Treaty and only a few months after Ludwig Erhard had assumed the chancellorship in West Germany, the level of friendliness had risen from about −.50 to about +.75. Franco-German amity appeared to be approaching the level of amicability that Western European states have for America. By way of contrast, developments between either France or West Germany and Italy were not of such great magnitude.

Figure 5.9, which shows changing British predispositions toward the European Economic Community countries as well as French, German,

---

[19] This is one point at which the use of a vector path for the entire decade may be misleading. The graphic representation of separate vector paths for the October, 1954, to October, 1958, period and the November, 1959, to February, 1964, period would show that the bulk of the increase occurred in the earlier period, and that by 1958 a plateau in mutual friendliness was reached that has been maintained since then. See the discussion by Karl W. Deutsch in Deutsch, Edinger, Macridis, and Merritt, *op. cit.*, pp. 218–51.

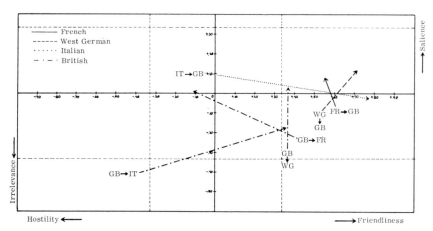

Figure 5.9. Mutual predispositions between Great Britain and EEC members

and Italian attitudes toward the United Kingdom, complements this picture. Franco-British relations on the mass opinion level became not only more unfriendly but also more salient—a trend which, if continued, could lead to outright hostility. By 1964 more British held unfavorable than favorable predispositions toward France; and, indeed, a smaller "friendliness gap" separated the Soviet Union and France in the British mind (.23 on the friendliness scale) than separated de Gaulle's Fifth Republic from either Italy (.46) or West Germany (.47), not to speak of the United States (.87). Great Britain meanwhile fell from first place in French affections in 1954 to fourth place a decade later, well ahead of the Soviet Union but behind West Germany, the United States, and Italy.

Anglo-German relations on the level of mass opinion seem to have been in a wait-and-see phase.[20] On the one hand, the countries became more interesting (salient) to each other; but, on the other, the level of friendliness did not increase to any great degree. The level of friendliness in British predispositions toward West Germany increased by only .002 from 1954 to 1964. The German friendliness index toward Britain increased by .17—an increase less than a seventh as great as that in German predispositions toward France.

The most significant gains in mutual friendliness shown on Figure 5.9

[20] See also Arnold J. Heidenheimer, "Einstellungen zu Deutschland in der britischen öffentlichen Meinung seit 1945," in *Die moderne Demokratie und ihr Recht: Festschrift für Gerhard Leibholz zum 65. Geburtstag*, ed. Karl Dietrich Bracher, Christopher Dawson, Willi Geiger, und Rudolf Smend (Tübingen: J. C. B. Mohr, 1966), pp. 151–77.

were between Italy and Great Britain. The Italian friendliness index toward the United Kingdom grew by .84; that of the British toward Italy by .74. America remained first in the hearts of both Italians and Britishers but, by 1964, Great Britain had risen from fourth to second place in Italian esteem and Italy had risen from fourth to third place in British predispositions (+.356 on the friendliness scale, only a shade below second-place Germany's score of +.364).

What these data suggest is that, for the decade between 1954 and 1964, mass relations among EEC members grew more cordial, whereas those between EEC members and Great Britain remained distant or grew more so. In both cases, however, Italy proved to be an exception. Indeed, the level of friendliness between Italians and Britishers increased at a greater rate than that between either of them and any other state. This special position of Italy in Western European public attitudes bears closer examination. For one thing, it would appear that during the course of the decade, Italy was becoming ever more an outsider among the three major EEC powers. Franco-German popular amity was proceeding at the cost of communality within the EEC. For another thing, cordiality of the British toward Italy increased commensurate with British hostility toward France and their relative coolness vis-à-vis West Germany. Whether these developments sprang from an Italian feeling that the Franco-German entente was too exclusive or from a British effort either to use Italy as a springboard for admission into the EEC group or as a means to prevent the EEC group from developing too rapidly, is a question that the data discussed here cannot answer. Similarly, the relationship between these trends in mass opinion and developments on the intergovernmental level—although of equal interest—is a topic that cannot be explored here. In evaluating such larger topics, however, underlying trends in mass opinion can offer valuable clues.

*Mathematical Applications
in Political Science, III*

was composed, printed, and bound by
Kingsport Press, Inc., Kingsport, Tennessee.
The paper is Warren's Cumberland Dull, and the
types are Monotype Modern No. 8 and Century
Bold Condensed.
Design is by Edward G. Foss.